MIXED FRUIT
FROM A SUSSEX TREE

ASPECTS
of
JOHN SNELLING

With a Preface by
Christina Maude

COUNTRY BOOKS

Published by Country Books
Courtyard Cottage, Little Longstone, Bakewell, Derbyshire DE45 1NN
Tel: 01629 640670
e-mail: dickrichardson@country-books.co.uk
www.countrybooks.biz
www.sussexbooks.co.uk

ISBN 978-1-910489-52-9

Printed and bound in England by 4edge Ltd., Hockley, Essex

Contents

Apologia – A Memoir

Apologia Plus

Death Drops in on the Rotary Club

After Wayne

Poems

Scripts for Sketches

Some Local History

Index

Preface

Imagine if you will a long train journey, during which you start chatting with the stranger opposite and realise later that a couple of hours have passed easily by, full of fascinating anecdote, light and shade, wit and wisdom; an all too rare treat in our hectic but increasingly isolated modern life. You part as new friends, vowing to stay in touch. That is how I felt on reading this little gem of a book for the first time. Storytelling in an easy conversational style. 'If you want to be a writer, write' was never more apposite than here. John has clearly been thinking and writing for most of his life, and the range of this collection is impressive. Social comedy, local history, the use of very different voices and some subtle and moving poetry.

The silver thread which runs through it all is that of a devoted and close family within and outside the Anglican church, with some deft pen-portraits of great men and women who made a largely unsung difference to many lives. As a record of vanished times, small scale and local, it will be an ornament to any social history collection, and it fulfils an important role in the fast-disappearing narrative on which future historians and biographers will come to rely.

Amusing, thought-provoking, puckish and intimate by turns, peopled by types whom we we will all know from our own lives, but never stereotypical, this is a quiet celebration of an English life which many of us will recognise with affection and nostalgia without ever wishing to turn back the clock.

Christina Maude

The Rotary Club of Horsham

Since part of this book was originally written for, or inspired by, the Rotary Club of Horsham, readers may like to learn a little more about it, without actually losing the will to live as a consequence.

-ooOoo-

What comes into your mind when you hear the word 'Rotary Club'? Some jolly chaps shaking plastic tins in the streets at Christmas, collecting cash for some good cause or other perhaps. There's more to Rotary than that, but it's a good place to start, because, in one word, this worldwide movement is *philanthropic*. The aim is to make life better for fellow humanity. It's a tall order, so where does one start? Well, there are umpteen ways – relieving poverty, improving health and education, fostering better understanding between countries. Sharing these aims with other people and getting together with them to achieve these aims can be fun and a way to forge lasting friendships. So there's a strong social ingredient to Rotary as well.

In 1905 a handful of Americans came together to use their position in local businesses and professions to make a difference to the quality of life wherever they could. From the beginning the use of one's vocation as a means of service was always uppermost. The idea of such clubs spread far and wide and quickly and became 'Rotary International' with its emblem a six-spoked gearwheel, a telling symbol since a gearwheel must mesh with others in order to perform.

By 1923 there were already Rotary clubs in Britain, and in that year the club in Chichester sponsored one in Horsham. The Horsham of 1923 was a 'small town' in every sense, with an urban population of a mere 12,500. The Great War was only five years in the past and there were still plenty of workhorses to be seen in the streets. (At least one GP had recently made his rounds on horseback.) The new club held its first meeting at the Black Horse, a hotel that stood on the junction of West Street and Worthing Road. The Club elected W.H.B. Lintott, a wholesale grocer, as its president and a solicitor, J.I. Eager its secretary. Other notable founder members were J.S. Whitehouse, who was the boss of Warnham Brickworks and Canon W.M. Peacock, Headmaster of Collyer's boys' grammar school. Until quite recent times Rotary clubs attempted to have only one representative from any calling, and that he should be either the top man of his outfit or at least to be in a very senior position. It was always 'he' because women were not eligible to join R.I. until later in te century. An Inner Wheel Club for widows, wives and daughters of Rotarians was formed in 1947 and thrives today. Women began to join the Horsham club as Rotarians in the century's new decade. A weekly Rotary meeting with a meal was a feature from the start, usually followed by a talk by a member or a guest. The meal was lunch, which suited a membership that worked in the town and could please themselves when they returned from lunch. Most clubs, including Horsham from 1989, now meet in the evening, or some even for breakfast. The Rotary constitution laid down that regular attendance was a 'must' and transgressors were thrown out.

The youthful Horsham club enthusiastically supported the ill-fated League of Nations, but in more recent times the spirit of internationalism has found expression in 'twinning' with Rotary clubs overseas. During the 'Great Depression' members formed their own internal labour exchange to give placements in their own businesses, especially to youngsters. Another early venture was to provide a social afternoon with tea and amusements for old men. It is noticeable how the early club's fairly basic and rudimentary efforts to 'do good' have been progressively taken over by the state, by other bodies or simply made irrelevant by social change. For example, a repeated event was to provide weekend hospitality in Horsham to foreign students brought down from London at a time when the sight of an African or an Asian person in Britain was then a novelty, but clearly a novelty no more.

In nigh on a century the members of the Rotary Club of Horsham must have embarked upon thousands of schemes and events in order to fulfil the aims of the movement's founders. Many have involved collecting money from a generous public, but it has to be acknowledged that Rotarians, their families and friends past and present have themselves been especially open-handed. Only a few of our first members have been mentioned here by name. The several hundred others will have to abide in the Club's records and dwell in the minds and memories of those who had the pleasure of knowing them.

Author's Introduction

Exposing oneself in public used to be an offence, and done in the old-fashioned, rather physical way, I believe that it still is. But in every other way everyone seems to be at it, via the printed word, radio, television, and the ever-growing 'social media' channels. No event or photograph is too asinine or too trivial to share with the rest of the world. And why not? Why be po-faced about it if doing it brings a ray of sunshine into somebody's *valle lacrimum?*

So in *Mixed Fruits* I shall follow in the trail of the receding herd, but do it my own way, not with *Facebook* or the like, but with words, which is the only way that I know. The section *Apologia* is largely autobiography, with a pervading thread chronicling the consequences of being a cradle Anglican. Auto-biographical snapshots are embedded in many other of my offerings. Here and there are also snatches of local history, and I'm afraid that references to the Rotary movement and to my town of Horsham do crop up rather a lot.

Elsewhere you will find what I hope are light-hearted essays written originally for the members of my Rotary Club, and from these, I suspect, you will come to your own conclusion as to the nature of the writer. You could call those 'oblique' autobiography.

There is another section which includes my short story called *After Wayne*. In this I try to live the life of someone completely outside of my personal experience. (I thought of describing this as 'an exercise in Christian empathy', but if

1

I did that not a soul would ever read it.) There is also a handful of poems mainly written following the death of my mother. But they are not all serious; as Samuel Johnson's friend remarked on trying to become a philosopher, 'cheerfulness kept breaking in.'.

Also somewhere in the book are four scripts of short sketches for television, written solely for my own amusement and never produced. The language of these and the language of *After Wayne* is demotic, but I hope not unduly offensive.

Finally, my sincere thanks go to Christina Maude for writing a Preface for me. In a busy life of public service she has made space for yet another act of charity.

John's Jottings

Past Particles

A priest friend of mine once told me that one of the worst of his priestly duties was to hear the confession of nuns – not because the poor dears had so many sins to confess but because what there were pretty small potatoes. (One can imagine the holy man sighing, 'Oh for the chance to hear the confession of a genocidal general or a mass-murderer once in a while!') Well, as we grow older we realize that everything is relative, so why do I feel a guilty pleasure of time-wasting by watching re-runs of Channel Four's *Time Team*? It's the programme where a few enthusiasts with impressive titles mess around with trowels and JCBs to find what's left of our ancestors and the places where they once lived and it's been going for years. In a way, it's reassuring to find that over those years that same Father Time who put those people and places under the feet of the archaeologists is now laying his hands on the experts themselves, with a few more grey locks here or an expanded waistline there with each successive series. How long before someone is scraping away the good earth to turn up *your* bones, Tony and Carenza? (That's an academic question, for ten-to-one neither Tony nor Carenza will return the compliment by being laid in earth but will be blasted up the chimney at Golder's Green or somewhere very like it. Which is pretty tough on their archaeologist successors.)

Ashes to ashes, dust to dust. One thing is certain, we can't blame Golder's Green for grounding me and a few hundred thousand others when we thought we were going to fly off on a holiday, and, even more importantly, wing it back again. The stuff that churns up from those holes in the ground we call volcanoes pre-dates practically anything else under the sun, until the next eruption. 'What is Man that Thou are mindful of him?' asks the psalmist. Put that question to the volcano and the answer comes back, 'I ain't mindful of you one little bit.' Just ask those folk in Pompeii. They still look decidedly ashen after their experience.

Perhaps those volcanoes that regularly throw dust in our eyes do some good after all, in cutting us down to size just a bit. It rather shows us that we can't organize or buy our way out of every problem, try as we may. We can sit around on airport floors and grizzle and moan about scientists, travel agents, politicians, grasping taxi drivers and 'other people'. The stark fact is simply that we've come bang up against Mother Nature, that old adversary that our ancestors have feared and respected since the earth began. Perhaps it's about time that we re-learnt how to do the same, with the same stoicism and dignity that our ancestors showed.

A Nasty Way To Go

According to Shakespeare, and he's probably right, when the evil Claudius wanted to get rid of Hamlet's father he dribbled something rather nasty into the old boy's earhole while he was having a quiet zizz. I've often wondered what that stuff might have been – not quite so caustic as Edward II's poker, but obviously just as effective. I always thought that maybe it was probably some acid or other, that sizzled right through the royal brainbox and straight out of the other ear, leaving not even enough of the 'leedle grey cells' in between to allow the King to wake up and remark, 'Is it my imagination, or is it getting a bit warm in here?'

Well, according to Google, which now seems to have replaced the Old and New Testaments and most of our reference libraries, it appears that the 'substance', as it would now be called, was *Habenon*. Surprisingly this is not the name of an O.T. prophet who enjoyed mithering the Children of Israel, but another name for henbane. This stuff, as the name implies, is bad news for chickens, and being a poisonous narcotic is not recommended for yoomans either. I just wonder how Claudius managed it. I doubt if grinding up a few henbane leaves, stalks or berries would give him enough jollop to cause the King much more than bit of deafness in one ear, and he would wake up fully refreshed next morning, demanding the full Danish with a side order of reindeer. I doubt if he would even think of calling for a beacon be lit to summon his personal otologist post haste to syringe the royal auditory orifice.

I realized the other day that somebody drizzles a concoction into my own ears fairly regularly. It's called *The Today Programme*, which starts as early as six o'clock, and before that there's a mishmash of stuff of which the Shipping Forecast is the most exciting. It's the best way of staying half-submerged in that delicious, warm swimming pool that exists between sleeping and waking. The only problem is that people in my dream, yes *my* dream, eventually start speaking in the tones of old John Humphrys, and then reality breaks in followed by the questions, 'What day is it and what the hell am I supposed to be doing today?' Well, I guess it doesn't matter that much – providing we all stay off the Habenon Eardrops.

All in A Name

I'm sure it's a sign of aging, but everyone keeps insisting on mentioning and showing pictures of people I have never heard of. Maybe I just don't read the right books, listen to the right music or see the right telly. Who are all these nasty-looking, overpaid low-life that I'm supposed to be interested in? A casual trawl of your average juvenile court would probably produce a remarkably similar catch.

I remember a reviewer of 'Ming' Campbell's auto-biography referring to him as 'the Tim Henman of politics', meaning a thoroughly decent fellow who 'lacked the killer instinct'. Leaving aside the fact that there already seem to be quite enough people roaming the streets more than ready to give that particular instinct full rein, in order to savour the comparison we at least need to know who Tim Henman is or was. If we are just thrown names we have never heard of, the exercise loses most of its point – so just try these on for size:

Dolly Tupper was the Andy Warhol of the Ely Cathedral Embroidery Guild. Jock McTavish was the Einstein of the

Aberdeen deep-sea fishing fleet. Rev. Bill Barnes was the Graham Norton of the Essex Model Railway Club. Jane Proudfoot was the Edith Piaf of the Chudleigh Farmers' Co-operative. Fred 'Goosy' Gander was the Alan Sugar of the Oakham Bible Fellowship. Selina Tibbs was the Jane Austen of the Abattoir and Meat Packers' Union. Mary Maltravers was the Cleopatra of the nursemaids of Kensington. Monica Scott-Handley-Grant-Scott was the Judas Iscariot of Roedean.

Need I go on? I can, of course, ad infinitum. But sooner or later, if not now already, we shall mention a real someone's name by accident. And if they get to hear about it, then look out! Fortunately, I think we're in the clear, as only Monica Scott-Handley-Grant-Scott might feel a bit aggrieved at being paired off with a Mr J. Iscariot, but even that un-fortunate fellow has had a makeover lately to 'undemonize' him. So no case to answer there, m'lud. And the original comparison? Ming Campbell and Tim Henman? Well, no problem there, surely. Unless, of course, between matches Tim pulled the wings off butterflies when no one was looking, or Ming Campbell is moonlighting round Auld Reekie's back streets collecting for loan sharks. That would certainly be a different story, and no doubt one that the tabloids would have ransacked the dustbins to find. At least, now the dustbin ransackers can have clean hands if not a pure heart, since with muck-raking on line no one needs to go within miles of a real dustbin.

The Last Time I saw Paris

I am ashamed to confess in this globe-trotting age that I have visited Paris only once, and that was for just two or three days on the way to the Loire Valley. It was many years ago, and I did about four things: a service at Notre Dame, visit the Louvre, go up to Sacre Coeur and walk along the Left Bank. My companion was the late Michael Cochrane, then Vicar at Holy Trinity Church in Horsham and also known to many Rotary families. As it was a real cheapo holiday by coach, we found ourselves in a pretty basic hotel in Montmartre, quite close to a sex shop, from which the vicar and the acolyte duly averted their eyes, of course. In those days there was no Swan Walk back home and certainly no Ann Summers to sanctify its north transept. We shared a large ground-floor room off the front hall, and couldn't help noticing how many couples came in and went straight up the stairs, the men often carrying what appeared to be bottles of (presumed) strong drink. Peering through a sort of ticket-office window, the receptionist/concierge might well have wandered in off the set of Maigret.

When I came to put my clothes into the empty wardrobe, I spotted a card carefully placed against the back of the cupboard. It turned out to be the photo of a young woman dressed in a glittery sort of frock. Even then the two innocents abroad didn't fully grasp its significance, and weren't sure quite what to do with it. In the end, I slipped it behind one of the several mirrors that were affixed to the bedroom walls. So this sister of mercy in the glittery frock was destined to be immured for ever by a couple of rather unsympathetic churchmen. How history repeats itself.

Forty-odd years on I feel that to 'lose' the girl's photo like that was a pretty mean and po-faced thing to do. I hope that today I'd be a bit more humane and show a bit more empathy. Though I sometimes wonder what would have happened if I'd taken the photo along to the 'ticket office' and handed it over to the gorgon. Would the girl in the glittery dress have suddenly appeared from a back room as a warm, breathing 20-year-old? Maybe. Or maybe at that moment would Inspector Maigret have emerged from the shadows to ask what I was doing with a photo of a girl who had just been strangled that very afternoon? As it was, the photo would have stayed where it was until the lot was bulldozed to make room for another sex shop. And by now the girl herself probably lies in some wretched cemetery somewhere in the arse-end of Paris. *Sic transit gloria...* glittery frocks and all.

On Books and Covers

'You can't tell a book by its cover'. How often have we heard that said? Book covers can certainly give a good idea of what lurks underneath them, but 'twasn't always thus. Two of my recent acquisitions both happen to be 'the book of the programme', namely Andrew Marr's *The Making of Modern Britain* and Diarmaid MacCulloch's *A History of Christianity*. One book bears an old- master painting of a robed Christ, hand raised in blessing, and the other a picture of the Union Flag. No one, except possibly an extra thick contestant on some daft quiz show could possibly confuse which cover goes with which book.

Well, it wasn't always like that, because from the earliest times books didn't have covers at all. The scribe's or the printer's job was to produce the pages, and someone else's to protect them from the thousand natural shocks that also books are heir to. Wooden boards or treated animal skins were pressed into service, and then, to avoid horrible mix-ups, someone had to write the name of the book on the outside. It wouldn't do at all to stretch out a hand to grasp Jeremy Taylor's *Holy Dying*, and find yourself with *Kama Sutra* – a mistake that some Seventeenth Century scholars may well have made. And then made it again and again perhaps. (Which thought raises an interesting speculation as to the kind of library that in those days might give room on its shelves to a Seventeenth Century devotional work cheek by jowl with a Sanskrit sex manual.)

Towards the end of the Eighteenth Century publishers produced their books without covers, so that the buyers could have them bound to order in a style to suit themselves, so the libraries of most historic houses will reflect the taste, or lack of it, of their owners. One would guess that this practice has now lapsed, although I recently bought a dozen examples of early Twentieth Century American fiction, all beautifully and uniformly bound with the previous owner's initials embossed in gold on the corner of every book. Although the man probably spent a sackful of dollars to achieve it, he almost certainly reduced the value of the books themselves, which would have been much more interesting to collectors in their original state and with their dust jackets.

Known in the trade as dust wrappers (abbreviated *dw*), people used to tear these off and bin them. Bad mistake. To be of any interest at all to collectors, first editions of modern fiction especially must always have their dws, the more pristine their condition the better. There's much more to be said on this subject, but as that happens to be the end of *my* page at least, we shall have to wrap up, dust and all.

'...That is for ever England...'

Scepticism increases with age, no doubt about it. So when they announced that Richard III's bones had been left in a long-stay car park in Leicester my response was a cynical 'Oh, yeah?'. But it all turned out to be true! The long-stay bit was certainly true, as he had been lying there since 1485 when what remained of him was taken there from Market Bosworth across the back of a horse. At that time the earth that received Richard lay under Greyfriars Church, which had been founded a bit over 200 years earlier by followers of St Francis of Assisi, members of the Order of Friars Minor, known as Greyfriars because of the colour of their habit. (It all gets most confusing, as a lot of Franciscans wore brown garb, and some favoured black – mercifully an issue that will never cause Facebook or Twitter to go into meltdown.)

Anyway, around 1495 the friars decided that Richard deserved something better than a hole in the ground, so had a whip-round to buy him a decent tomb. Even Richard's adversary, aka Henry VII, chipped in. The result was a nice alabaster job inset with coloured stones, but it wasn't there long, as Henry VIII's Tudor equivalent of a bulldozer made short work of Greyfriars and umpteen similar places when he laid flat the monasteries. So the hand of time eventually turned Richard's last resting place into a pay-and-display.

A fierce argument raged whether Richard of York should be taken to York to rest in peace. That seems a reasonable proposition – after all, being in Leicester at all was a bit of an accident, and would anyone having the misfortune to perish, say, on the M4 really expect to end up buried in some bone-yard in Swindon? Yet I for one have warmed to Leicester's claim and eventual triumph. It's a city with a significantly high immigrant population who know little of Richard or the history of England and don't want to know and never will know. So why not let those *other folk* of Leicester make the most of their connexion with their English past? Why not let Leicester Cathedral become a centre of pilgrimage for the Richard the Third Society and anyone else equally eccentric? Perhaps one day Leicester's Cathedral will resemble the old abbey at Ely in the days of Hereward, a reminder of a vanishing England, rising through clouds of unknowing and just catching the last rays of a dying sun.

1904 Poster Boy

Horsham's Museum holds a fascinating collection of that most ephemeral of art forms – the poster. A newspaper may hope for a resurrection as a wrapper for the national dish, but for the poster it's *dies irae* is built-in. So we're lucky to see a poster of a handsome young man with his name boldly emblazoned underneath – TURNOUR. This was no matinée idol of the silent movies but Eddie Turnour the Tory candidate at a by-election to be held in Horsham in the year 1904. He was merely 21, but naturally enough for a Tory candidate in 1904, his credentials were impeccable. His dad was the Fifth Earl Winterton and his mum the daughter of the first Duke of Abercorn, but as the titles were all Irish a seat in the House of Lords did not go with them. Of course, Eddie won the seat and became the 'baby' of the house. The remarkable thing was that he stayed there until he became the 'father' of the House, and retired in 1951.

As a schoolboy in Horsham after the war, and a member of the Young Conservatives, I had ample opportunity to observe the member for Horsham. Lord Winterton's physical appearance was striking, as every bit of him seemed to have been stretched on some medieval rack, with a long skull and a tall almost emaciated-looking body. I had never seen anyone with longer fingers. I guess that the bones of his middle finger were all three inches long. As he was partial to wearing double-breasted suits closely buttoned across his torso, these served to enhance his towering stature. His public speaking style was quite distinctive, as he would frequently fold his long, gangling arms across his chest or stick his hands into his coat pockets, thumbs facing forward. I can't remember that his audience ever 'rolled in the aisle' in paroxysms of mirth.

13

Just as happens today, poor old Winterton in some distant past had allegedly made some terrible gaffe, which his political opponents would never let him forget and would throw back at him whenever they had the chance. He was once supposed to have said something like 'A herring should be quite sufficient for a working man's dinner'. Coming from someone who quite clearly appeared to enjoy the best of everything that a life of privilege could offer, Winterton's herring rather stuck in the throat of many a working man, and so did neither of them any good. Perhaps he never even uttered those words, although I have a feeling that he probably said something very like them. Winterton was a creature of his era and his social milieu, as, indeed, we all inescapably are. His may have been 'a life of privilege', but I saw him arrive at meetings driving himself in a rather horrible Ford Prefect, perhaps a pointer to an innate frugality. Who knows, maybe he actually enjoyed the occasional herring for dinner himself?

These reminiscences are sadly only too superficial, the tip of the Winterton iceberg visible to a young outsider. By all accounts, below the waterline was a man albeit of limited ability, yet brave and loyal, and an engaging raconteur one would have liked to have known. But touchy feely he wasn't, and one can't help wondering what he would make of the political and social scene today, not least how his own party has changed since that day when his long, narrow coffin was laid in the earth of Kirdford while a lone huntsman sounded the call 'Gone Away'.

A bit of fun from 2008

Here are some recent press reports. How many are genuine?

1) Ken Livingstone is to provide £250,000 from London's community budget to sponsor goat racing along the Thames towpath from Putney to Mortlake. It will be known as Ken's University Goat Race. Mr Livingstone will personally ritually slaughter the winner.

2) A statement by Boris Johnson: 'Would I ritually slaughter a goat? Gosh oh golly. Mmm… Cripes, that's a hard one, as the actress …oh golly. Why do you guys give me all the nasty questions? I suppose I'd slit the throat of a bloody goat if I had to, but I bet there's some Euro reg. or other against it. What? There isn't? Oh, bugger! Must run…'

3) The Lord Mayor of London overheard after a Mansion House dinner:
'Why does that twerp down the road keep boasting about what he's done for London? Up this end is where the dosh is made – that silly sod only knows how to spend it. And will the Alderman who's sitting on the port please pass it up here!'

4) From the Vatican Press Office
This office knows nothing of plans to revive the title of Holy Roman Emperor, or of Mr Blair having had his first fitting of the diadem and the robes.

5) *Sun* headline: 'Prescott Pongs Made Me Puke'.
'There was no way my wife and I could move into the accommodation,' sniffed Lord Malloch-Brown. 'What with Pauline's perfumes and John's pies, only deep cleaning and complete fumigation could make it habitable. They must have been horribly working class. Thank God New Labour have seen off people like that. 'Persons of the oik persuasion,' Trish calls them.

6) A spokeswoman for the body of professional psychiatrists has denied that Mr Al Fayed has applied for membership, but added that any application would be carefully considered.

7) A local newspaper has confirmed that 98% of its readership bought the paper solely for the death announcements. The other 2% bought it by mistake.

A Blooming Miracle – Eighty Years On!

If I asked 'Where were you on 6TH May 1935?', most readers will reply, 'I wasn't anywhere, because I just *was* not.' Well, I can tell you where *I* was – gazing from an upper window of an ancient house in The Causeway in Horsham to watch the great and the good of the town enter St. Mary's to celebrate the Silver Jubilee of King George V. And it's a good job that we all did what we did when we did it because it wasn't long before the said King and Emperor would be laid to rest at Windsor.

But on that May day I was where I was because my family knew the Parish Clerk, whose 'tied cottage' the house was. In fact, it was one of three adjoining cottages that would shortly be sold, renovated and turned into that single, magnificent and venerable residence we know today as *Minstrels*. Had I gone into the garden that day I would have found an exuberant and rather wild oasis right in the middle of ancient Horsham, a cottage garden, like the house itself, dating back maybe five hundred years. And in the middle of it all I would have found the red and white flowers of peonies in bud. How do I know that? Well, the Parish Clerk was not long in following his king to a some-what more modest resting place in Hills Cemetery, and his widow offered the peony plants to my mother. So they were duly dug up and re-planted at Horsham's Nelson Road. And forty years after that we dug them up again and moved them half a mile to where they were re-planted. And there they are today, fighting for their lives against opposition just as exuberant as before, but this time in a less prestigious setting than Horsham's Causeway.

Perhaps our chemists should be discovering the long-life genes that lurk in our gardens. I know for certain that one of my rose bushes is over fifty years old and another over forty, and my sycamores probably started life bordering an open field. But we all know that trees are another story and we had better leave it there. But I'll wager one thing – that the oak of King George's coffin would have been much, much older than he was when it was felled, and carefully matured and seasoned in order to fulfil its destiny – to hold the mortal remains of George Frederick Ernest Albert, King and Emperor.

Bon Appétit!

Umpteen years ago my family discovered an attractive restaurant in Worthing and for years afterwards that was the place we always went whenever we found an excuse to celebrate something. The head waiter was an imposing figure, who walked with a slight limp, and I always believed that it was the weight of the gold and specie in his pocket that made him lop-sided. The establishment provided paper napkins, the heavy sort that are almost impossible to tear, and this gave our *major domo* a means of buttering up those clients most likely to increase his angle of inclination from the vertical. Once his targets were seated he would tower over their table, click his fingers at the nearest minion and call in a loud voice, 'Bring *linen* napkins to this table!' Whereupon, of course, he would personally snap open the finest napery and ceremoniously lay it across the knees of the favoured if slightly bewildered patrons. (Thereafter, of course, the cry 'Bring *linen* napkins to this table!' became a family catchphrase, reserved mainly for use on grossly in-appropriate occasions.)

All this was brought to mind by the realization that nowadays I seem to find it impossible to steer food in the direction of the mouth without distributing half of it down whatever I happen to be wearing. A brand new sweater? Splosh, there goes a great gobbet of chicken curry. A white shirt? A few splashes of red wine are quite enough. A rarely-worn silk tie? Yuk, that looks like Greek yoghurt. A similar disaster is to unload the dishwasher without due care and grab a glass that has fallen over and collected water. The water, of course, unerringly ends up on the crotch area one's trousers just before a visitor rings the doorbell.

On T/V old Hercule Poirot seems to have had the answer. Whenever we see him eating, he first grabs something resembling a small bedsheet and tucks it well into his collar, and the remarkable thing is that it never falls out. Anything that I attach to my own collar or even waistband at once falls to the floor and is instantly trampled underfoot firstly by me and then by a whole tableful of diners. At home, of course, a bib would be the answer, preferably the kind of bib favoured by those who normally sit in a high-chair and use a pusher, a pusher kept not for eating but exclusively for banging the tray in front of them. That's the answer! One of those plastic bibs with a gutter at the bottom to catch what evades the mouth. So get lost, smarmy head waiters! Who needs you or your linen napkins! 'Bring a *bib* to this table!!'

Choose Your Weapons

When I was a boy at the grammar school, what scared me more than the risk of a beating from the headmaster was an obligation to speak at the Debating Society. I would have been about 16, so by that age I really should have had a good deal more *savoir faire*. Allowing that I was probably 'young for my age', just look at today's sixteen-year-olds to see how far adolescents have come on since then – now they all seem to be self-assured and worldly-wise. How I wish I'd had a bit of that back then.

Surprisingly, our Debating Society was not invented by the Devil himself, but by a wise old owl of a headmaster trying to turn tongue-tied clods of Sussex boys into more articulate clods of Sussex men. My own very first contribution to a debate was 'I think Mr So-and-So has hit the nail on the head'. Just a cliché from beginning to end. But it sufficed, and in his humanity and charity the 'Old Man' allowed it to count as a speech, and I was off the hook until my turn came round again.

Our debating subjects were predictable. We even waxed philosophical with *'The pen is mightier than the sword'*, which even today is more than likely to be slipped into A-level essay questions by examiners too tired or too lazy to focus their 'trained minds' on anything more original. (I sometimes think that if I'm one of those who's supposed to have a trained mind, then it doesn't always feel like it, and God help the others!)

Yet the pen versus sword debate is a live issue. Being on the side of the angels (of course) and ever hopeful, we chime in unison 'No question, the pen is always mightier than the sword. We have The Bible and the great works of civilization. These will always triumph'. Oh yeah. Really? Tell that to the slaughtered masses of China, Russia, Europe, Zimbabwe, Syria, in fact just about anywhere you care to look. Yes, look at British history too. What's the use of a good book to a man whose eyes stare from a head that a broadsword has just lopped off his shoulders?

We should go back to Edward Bulwer Lytton whose words they are, and look hard at the first line of his couplet:

Beneath the rule of men entirely great
The pen is mightier than the sword

So where are those 'entirely great' men to do the ruling, and lift our hearts and make it all come good? Halloo, is there anybody out there?...Anyone...?

Denne Hill Pilgrims

While browsing the internet the other day looking for something on Mohammed, I stumbled across a link to a website asking the question, 'Called to be a monk, nun or priest? Take free online test to see if God is calling you.' I declined to take the test. Well, suppose at the end of it all I heard the voice of God booming away like Joss Acland in an echo chamber: 'You're just the kind of person we're looking for, John. What would you like to be – monk, nun or priest? I'll send someone round. But for now be good, and don't do anything I wouldn't do.'

As it happens, I did once dress up as a Benedictine monk for a school play – a great part, as I was in sole charge of the distillery. And later when I was training to become a C of E lay reader (later aborted) I did occasionally have to wear most of the clerical gear except the dog collar. Although vocations to the nunhood have fallen away, taking the veil to redress the balance is fortunately ruled out for chaps, and anyway the medical might prove a bit of a challenge. (*Doctor to Mother Superior:* 'Would you come in here a moment, Reverend Mother. There's something rather unusual about this postulant....' *Reverend Mother comes in and faints, but manages to say:* 'Blimey, Doc!') Needless to say, the Head Nun is played by Hattie Jacques, the doctor by Peter Butterworth and the postulant by Charles Hawtrey. Was there ever a *Carry On Nunning*? Let's hope not.

Back to Mohammed. I was checking on the saying about Mohammed and the mountain. Apparently the mountain was Mount Safa in Saudi Arabia, and it's really not much more than a hill in Mecca, but for Muslims it's a pretty important place. Old Horshamites regarded Denne Hill in much the same if more earthly light, as a favourite place to walk on in summer and to toboggan down in snowy winters. I've done both, and coming down the hill on a sledge at full pelt is a pretty hair-raising experience. Right at the bottom, if you ever got as far as that, there was an iron fence, considerately bent back around the centre so that tobogganers would not hit its bars and end up like a potato going through a chipper. It's sad to see Denne Hill now invaded by bracken and demoted as a fun place for Horsham people. I seem to remember stories of gatherings and fetes being held on 'the Hill', probably in those days before the town acquired Horsham Park in the 1920s. Perhaps it's better left as it is. After all, we don't want millions of Sussex pilgrims making it Horsham's version of Mount Safa and go marching round it, pausing only accidentally to trample under foot a few thousand unfortunate fellow devotees in the process, do we?

Disillusion

I thought we'd give the critical review of O.G.M a miss this week, and turn to something else. O.G.M. is 'Our Great Movement' and, of course, by that I mean Rotary. But over the years the supporters of a good many movements have modestly referred to their causes thus. In the post-war years the phrase was rarely off the lips of Labour Party and Trade Union orators, a little less so on Tory tongues. Perhaps the Tories just knew by instinct they were born to rule and didn't feel the need flatter themselves by referring to their own greatness. Well, with a bit of luck, both parties have now had at least some of their self-satisfied stuffing knocked out of them by defeat and failure. But there's still a long way to go before real humility takes its place.

As many of my generation were, I was born to be respectful and naively deferential to great swathes of the population – Royalty, aristocracy, landowners, all professionals, successful small businessmen in a bigger way than my own family, and, good grief, even members of this Rotary Club whose names appear early on in our list of Past Presidents. Many of those people deserved all the respect and deference I gave them. But as I grew to man's estate and got around a bit I started to see a very different side to the great and the good. In many instances the phrase 'whited sepulchres' springs to mind. All this self-abasement before so many idols, but, stay awhile, what's this I see at ground level? Can it be, no, surely not? These feet are not the feet of idols – they are of clay! *Clay! Clay!*

This process of disillusionment is, I fear, part of the ageing process and is equally relentless. What a shock to discover that so many emperors are going around the place stark-bollock naked. And not a few empresses as well, although I can't immediately think of the proper (or even an improper) description for their condition.

To close – just an example of a recent shock to my system. (Incredulity at today's political antics is excluded, or this article will never end.) In a recent television series about Luther, written and presented by 'an historian'. he was describing how Luther needed to go under cover. To this end, said the 'historian', Luther *'grew a false beard'*. I would dearly like to know how he did that, because in my experience false beards are bought and affixed with spirit gum. Actually growing them is new to me. How could anyone even think such a laughable phrase, let alone write it and then say it out loud in public? He should have been struck by lightning on the spot. On the contrary. Today that same man has been promoted and is pre-eminent among our (pardon the cliché) 'cultural elite'.

Getting the hump with Sir Joshua

Around 1788 Sir Joshua Reynolds painted a portrait of a young girl and called it *The Age of Innocence*. I believe it's in the Tate Gallery, but I've never seen it, though a reproduction of it must be the first painting that I ever set eyes on. When my mum and dad were first married in 1929 they bought an art magazine which gave away coloured prints, a few of which they framed. Gainsborough's so-called *Blue Boy* was another one. I am still astonished that a young couple starting out in life on Two Pounds Ten Shillings a week should have aspired to such cultural heights, being, as any modern politician would designate them, 'ordinary hard-working people'. I wonder, after the billions and billions of pounds that have been spent on education and self-consciously 'bringing culture to the masses' since 1929, I wonder what today's newlyweds hang in their first home – a boy band poster perhaps, or possibly a David Hockney print from the Swimming Pool series, or at a pinch a Lowry street scene maybe. I'm not knocking the choice of a Hockney or a poster for today's newlyweds. But I cannot help reflecting that by 1929 a lot less money and fewer resources had gone into fashioning the taste of my parents than the taste of a similar couple today. I guess that a lot depends on where you start from and whether nature or nurture gets the upper hand.

Actually, at the age of two or three I found the Reynolds girl rather unsettling. The demure young lady is seated looking to her left, with a full creamy-coloured skirt billowing out around her down to the floor. The picture used to hang at the top of the stairs, and gazing up to it from the bottom step it didn't look at all like a girl in a dress at all but, thanks to the full skirt and its colour, more like the head of a weirdly menacing camel-like creature. A child's

25

imagination had made something completely benign into something pretty scary. But I never told my mum and dad that.

Ghosts

This time I thought that we might get a bit spiritual. Don't panic, I'm not going to hold you with a skinny hand like Coleridge's Ancient Mariner, then get you kneeling on a non-denominational prayer mat. This is about apparitions, manifestations or ghosts. Have you ever seen one? I don't think that I have, though it's said that often they look quite normal and at the time we think they're real. Three of my relatives, all now deceased themselves, were convinced that they had – one of them was up a tree in Horsham's Causeway of all places – the vision was up in a tree, that is, not the witness. (The idea of a thing in a tree is a bit spooky for starters.) I also know a man who has seen the phantom that's said to walk in the road at Buck Barn on the road to Worthing.

I'm certain that many of these sightings are simply aberrations of the brain, caused by the slightest chemical imbalance somewhere, with a thousand and one different causes. Often a few microseconds of sleep can leave behind the will o' the wisp of a dream that we then can't reconcile with being awake. But what about poltergeists and psychokinesis? These appear to be rather better authenticated, so where do they fit in?

What fascinates me is this – why are ghosts, (assuming

for now that there are such things), always fully clothed? As the funeral service says, we come into the world with nothing and we can take nothing out. So why aren't our ghosts walking around starkers? (Perhaps the prospect of a young nun rising up in the altogether might do wonders for ghost hunting.) What's so special about a wimple, or a bodice or an old pair of leather shoes that they too should re-appear along with their wearer? Why is the Napoleonic soldier said to have been seen walking about in a long great-coat near the Cricket Field in Horsham not just a naked bloke walking about? (Unless, maybe, he was really just a rough sleeper wandering up from Chesworth.)

If there is an explanation for robed apparitions, can it be that the vision being picked up is being passed on from someone else's contemporary perception of it? But since it's on the cards that the original perceiver of that image is also laid in earth somewhere, this idea floats like a lead-lined coffin.

Well, personally, I'm not bovvered. Am I bovvered? No, just curious. And it was curiosity that killed the cat, of course. Now would that be the grey cat that my Canadian cousin used to see walking around indoors, though she didn't have a cat and all her doors and windows were shut?

Just Words

Sixty years or so ago there was a sage called Ivor Brown, who kept his readers amused with little books about words and their meanings. Admittedly they were what's known as 'slim volumes', but wouldn't it be great if we could still buy anything like them, published by Jonathan Cape in hardback as these were, for a mere 30p each in today's equivalent coinage! (Yes, yes, we all know there's no real comparison, since to Ivor Brown's book buyer a wage of eight quid or so a week was reckoned pretty good.) Well, one of the words that I.B. wrote about was kiosk, and he quoted a chairman of the former Horsham Rural District Council no less to make his point. Apparently, this anonymous councillor fulminated against the word kiosk in the belief that it was Russian, and that in stamping on all things marked 'made in USSR' he was making his own modest contribution to victory in the Cold War. Old Ivor delightedly pointed out that the H.R.D.C. chairman was way off target, as kiosk is not a Russian word at all, but denoted a rather sumptuous pavilion from Turkey or Persia, long before the days of 'Uncle Joe' and his ilk. Today, our kiosks dispensing Coke or burgers are a far cry from the ancient pleasure domes of brocaded satraps, sitting pavilioned in splendour, like the 'Ancient of Days'.

While on the subject of words, aren't we all completely fed up with our politicians 'rolling out' or 'launching' 'a raft' of measures? It always reminds me of Géricault's powerful and rather disturbing painting,'The Raft of the Medusa'. If it reminded our politicians of the same thing they'd just go off somewhere and quietly throw up and never use the phrase again. And while we're at it, where have all the 'turning points' gone? They've suddenly morphed into 'tipping points'. This slightly changes the image, because, to me anyway, turning takes place on a horizontal plane, while tipping is on a vertical one. As everything nice seems to be going down and everything nasty is going up, maybe a vertical shift is now a highly appropriate fancy. And until a few years ago we were not yet 'out of the wood'. Today we are not satisfied with a single wood, because for some reason they're now always in the plural. It's always 'the woods' that we're struggling to get out of. In spite of all Macbeth's tribulations, Birnam Wood obstinately remained in the singular, resisting all temptation to pile on the agony by replicating itself. Maybe once again the Bard had it right. Less is usually more.

K492

It's funny how the oddest things touch off a memory. Watching *The Marriage of Figaro* from Covent Garden on BBC Four, I was transported back to the first time I'd ever heard any Figaro. I would have been rising fifteen or so and at Collyer's School in Horsham, then a grammar school. There was one particular subject where I always registered my 'personal worst', for ever coming 27TH out of a class of 27. (Although in one year I put on a great spurt and ended up at no. 26) This subject was called 'Manual' and at Collyer's at that time that word simply meant 'woodwork'. Nowadays, no doubt, boys and girls can learn how to build a nuclear reactor or a cathedral in an afternoon double-period, but in my day it was woodwork or nothing. In fact, there was even precious little of that, because, as the master in charge was always bewailing, 'we can't get the wood!' Well, it was war time. So the boys who were half capable – not me, obviously – spent their time trying to repair the school's broken chairs that flowed in to the workshop in a constant stream, some of them probably dating from the 1920s or 1930s and far too fragile for the backsides of boys who could range from weedy eleven-year-olds to giants who within months might be driving a tank or crewing a warship. The workshop glue-pot, sitting atop an ever-burning stove, was constantly fed by chunks of brown stuff resembling hard toffee. Boys then enthusiastically applied the resulting gunge to anything within reach, the broken bits of chairs, the floor, their clothes, and, of course, themselves.

The master who ran the workshop was a devotee of the gramophone and his collection of shellac records that spun around at 78 rpm., and he once invited three of us boys to his house in Salisbury Road to be educated into the pleasures of 'good music'. I can't now remember whether his gramophone was wind-up or electric, but I'm pretty sure that it had two little doors at the front, so that when not in use the machine's more private parts could be genteelly screened from the gaze of rough Calibans such as us. One of the bits he played us was the aria from the end of Act 1 of *Marriage of Figaro* where Figaro tells Cherubino of the great time he will be having in the army. And what did we boys make of it? Well, not much. Suppressing the occasional teenage giggle we tried not to look too bored and couldn't wait for our release. Since then, I've seen and heard *The Marriage of Figaro* in all sorts of settings and have been utterly transported by every minute of it. So was this change down to the kindly educational efforts of an earnest woodwork master all those years ago? Nope, not a bit of it. It happened just because all kids grow up. Equally, some adults never do.

Monkey Business

When I was a lad, my father sometimes bought a copy of a small-ads paper called *Exchange and Mart*. I'm not sure why, since as far as I know he never once bought or sold anything as a result. But I was fascinated by it, because at the time I was desperate to own a monkey and regularly turned the pages to scan the monkey bargains. But my parents were adamant – definitely *no* monkey! (I think that my dad had taken against monkeys from that day when members of a monkey tribe severely embarrassed him in front of my mother and her mother as they walked past the monkey cage at the zoo. (What *were* they doing? One guess would probably be enough.)

Well, how times change. Now, at the age I am, I would absolutely hate having a monkey as a pet, in fact for me now any pets of any description indoors are an utter no-go area. Perhaps I've become a victim of the hygiene police, but the mere thought of opening my doors to half of Creation in the form of fleas, ticks, lice, mites, pee and poo is pretty unthinkable. So it's strange that I remain a sucker for dogs. When I meet one, we look each other in the eyes and at once I feel united with a soul-mate, especially the old dogs, those stiff in the leg, grey around the muzzle and eyes, those who are always lost in thought gazing towards some distant horizon, just playing a waiting game, pushing the bowl around the floor a bit, then a little finicky eating, slobbering noisily over the water, then a lot of sleeping. It's a dog's life, but don't mock it. It's the life of many of us.

I'm just grateful that when I was mad about having a monkey I wasn't a bit older and shopping for a 'significant other'. On the everlasting learning-curve, would we both have later wanted to take the goods back to the shop – just as I went off monkeys? We're now celebrating Darwin's anniversary and his Evolution, and, true to form, the BBC is running it all to death so that I for one wish to hear nothing more about it for another century. And I'm certainly not going to be one of the hordes trampling over the flaming Galapagos Islands and ruining them. For Heaven's sake, just leave the ruddy place alone and be prepared to take it all as read.

Nevertheless, clever old Darwin revealed the unstoppable power of the evolutionary thrust and the change it both demands and creates. Since *homo sapiens* and his institutions strongly prefer to hang on to the status quo, said ***hom. sap.*** was never likely to have an easy ride. Thanks to Evolution, we now all have much more food for thought than any old grizzled dog or those rude monkeys who made my dad blush at Chessington all those years ago.

No Place Like It!

'Home is where the heart is.' Apparently it was Pliny the Elder who first came up with this felicity, and if memory serves me right, this was the same old codger who really enjoyed the spectacle of Vesuvius blowing its top, right up until it dropped a few tons of hot ashes on his head, whereupon he completely lost interest in vulacanology as a subject of study. Can't you just imagine early Hollywood's treatment of the scene in a Pliny biopic?

Mrs. Pliny: *"Come inside, Pliny the Elder; don't stand out there on the patio watching the eruption of Vesuvius in 79 AD. Come into the villa now and have a typical Roman supper, lying on a low day-bed and drinking wine from an elaborately-fashioned goblet."*

Pliny: *"Wait wife, I'm just observing the natural phenomena, a practice for which I shall one day be famous."*

Although Pliny senior may not have run fast enough to escape the mighty Vesuvius, he was bang-on with his observation on home and heart, which only goes to show that sages and philosophers may not be our first choice for the 100-metre Olympics.

Pliny clearly implies that heart and home may not always cosily co-habit the same space. Diligent study of history programmes on TV and the occasional dalliance with a real book will show that some people were moving about the face of the globe a few thousand years before a certain couple and their neonate made their own journey from Bethlehem to Nazareth (or was it Egypt?). And since then people have milled around like demented ants on a thundery afternoon and travelled even further. 'And God stretched forth his hand and invented Ryanair, and God saw it and moved on quickly.' So it's hardly surprising that today millions of people living in one place look across the seas to other places they choose to call 'home'. What else explains St. Patrick's Day in New York, Burns Night in Vancouver, or why the Raj just loved his tea dances up-county at Simla? That's the fun side. The dark side, of course, is cruelty, war and ethnic cleansing.

I'm one of the lucky ones. For me heart and home have never been torn asunder. Zoom in on England, zoom in on Sussex, and then for fine tuning give me the Arun Valley, say from Pulborough down to Arundel. For me, that little piece of Sussex landscape is my blessed plot, my Shangri-La, my El Dorado, my Mecca, my St. Patrick's Day, my Burns Night, my Simla tea dance, all rolled into one.

Playing silly bloggers from 2009

I haven't the slightest idea of what 'blogs' are, though I keep on hearing and reading about them. One suspects that it's the modern, electronic version of men exposing themselves to unsuspecting passers-by in Horsham Park. It happened to my cousin once when she was about twelve, and it made such an impression on her that she completely forgot about it and didn't mention it to her mother for another week. By then, of course, everything, yes everything, had gone cold. One assumes that the unkindest words a policeman could utter on arresting a flasher is, 'Move along everybody, there's nothing to see here'.

And now after blogs there's something called 'Twitter'. Heaven knows what that is. I always thought it was just something that sparrows did. Now my paper tells me that blogs and twitters are to be taught in primary schools. (Presumably all this will replace boring old subjects like spelling and arithmetic.) And this thing called 'FaceBook' is something else, but I believe our gracious Majesty has now joined, or more likely one of her androgynous minions has signed up for her. I'm still not sure what message this is sending us – either that this FaceBook thing is 'a boon and a blessing to men', or it's now time to sell our entire holding in Monarchy UK.

The other day a lady telephoned to ask if she could come and service my Dyson. I really should have agreed and told her that it's in the cupboard under the stairs. In a bungalow she would have found it hard to find, even with her satnavs, of which I'm sure she has many. Eventually I would tell her that I don't possess a Dyson. She wouldn't see the joke, and I would receive a bill for a £90 call-out charge, no doubt with the bailiffs hiding just round the corner. The same lady later rang my cousin's number, the same cousin who showed such *sang-froid* in Horsham Park as a girl. I was sitting with her in the nursing home where thanks to multiple sclerosis she can barely move a single muscle. She hasn't been able to do anything for herself for some years, so an offer to service her Dyson was even more fatuous than the call that I had. And, like me, she had never owned a Dyson anyway. I always try to see the underlying logic behind things that happen, but this one defeats me. I understand that 'blogs' are a favourite vehicle for whistle- blowers who want to spill the beans on their employers. Now if there's a blog that tells me which lunatic company squanders its money on point-less phone calls like those, then that's a blog I *might* read.

Saving Saint Joan

Walk down West Street on Saturday, and ask people at random what they think of G.B.S. Some may say, 'What group is she with?' while others will start praising their *Tom Tom*, which never lets them down. And some will know that G.B.S. were the initials of George Bernard Shaw, the dramatist and writer who dominated the English and American stage for almost half of the Twentieth Century. Shaw's story is a fascinating one. Born into a genteely poor family in Dublin in 1856 with a boozy father and an artistic music-teacher mother, early life must have been a struggle. But his was a classic case of 'late development' because, largely self-taught, when he arrived in London he had developed a formidable intellect. By the time he died in 1950 the best was long over, but in between he had been the Alan Ayckbourn, Samuel Beckett and Alan Bennett of the age all rolled into one.

So what has happened to his work? His plays, once as

eagerly awaited as any new offering fom the pen of Andrew Lloyd Webber, are not often now performed. Even that great film *My Fair Lady*, based on his play *Pygmalion*, must be reaching its sell-by. Arguably his most serious play, *Saint Joan*, is now collecting the dust. First performed in New York in 1923, Sybil Thorndike played Joan the Maid of Orleans who had been just nineteen when she was burnt at the stake for heresy. One wonders whether it unduly stretched the imagination of the New York audience to see the nineteen-year-old being played by a woman of forty-one. (When I saw Dame Sybil myself at Chichester over forty years later she was still going strong, though admittedly by then playing Saint Joan would have been a bit beyond her.)

It's said that when someone asked Shaw why he had written *Saint Joan*, he replied, 'To save her from John Drinkwater'. Nowadays the name of John Drinkwater is almost unknown, and in retrospect one wonders why Shaw mentioned his name. Well, Drinkwater had been a fairly prolific dramatist, who in 1918 had staged his historical play *Abraham Lincoln*, followed by *Oliver Cromwell* in 1921. So maybe Shaw feared that Drinkwater may have been on the look-out for another suitable historical subject and was afraid that he'd shoot his fox. Anyway, G.B.S. got there first. It's all water under the bridge now. And all a bit sad. Drinkwater has sunk without trace. Shaw had made a tidy sum from his writings, and when he died he left the residue of his estate to promote a new alphabet consisting of no less than forty letters. And, as we know, that idea, like Drinkwater's plays, now also lies at the bottom of the briny

Silver Linings

A vicar friend of mine used to tell a rather hilarious story of his attempt to meet the wishes of a parishioner by burying the old man's ashes at sea. He was only too grateful that challenging the waves of a choppy English Channel in a rowing boat only ever came his way that once. But even land-locked funerals can have their lighter moments. Once, when giving the address, or 'eulogy' as it's now often called, I remarked how nice it was that the deceased son's wife was now 'expecting'. A gratifying murmur rippled across the crematorium chapel. As we were leaving, the priest leant across and whispered to me, 'You made the wrong girl pregnant, old boy.' And, right enough, it was the daughter of the departed who was, how shall we say, 'up the duff', not his daughter-in-law. The wonder is that my shock announcement had caused only a ripple and not a full-scale riot! Just suppose we'd been in Ireland? Or maybe Pakistan? Fortunately, most of the mourners knew that the error was mine, and kindly said my gaffe had lightened the mood no end. But, even so, my red face lasted for days.

At a funeral very recently I was seated in front a strong soprano who early on in the first hymn lost her place and throughout was singing the verse in front of everyone else, so that when she was beseeching the Lord to hold his cross before her dying eyes, the rest of us were still ploughing on, fearing no foe with Thee on hand to bless. We all knew that the truth would dawn on this dedicated diva when she ran out of road as everyone else started on the last verse. For about half a line silence fell on this Callas of the crematoria. Would she sit righteously silent while all those schismatic singers around her persisted in their error? No, she soon tumbled that the game was up, so off she went again stronger than ever, giving the Lord even yet another chance to hold his cross up before her eyes and to point her to the skies, *et cetera*. All this rather raises the question of whether strong, and possibly overconfident, singers ever actually listen to what anyone else is singing. One imagines that sometimes instrumentalists can fall into the same trap

Most clergypersons I have ever known usually have a treasure trove of funny stories to tell about funerals, and to a lesser extent about marriages and baptisms, in fact any occasion when the man on the Clapham Omnibus exchanges his seat for an unfamiliar pew or chair in a place of worship. It's usually a re-run of the Ascot scene from *My Fair Lady*, except it's in a different context, and never, *ever* designed by Cecil Beaton.

Spin Doctors and Child Poverty

We seem to hear a lot about 'Child Poverty' these days, but only in the last ten years or so. It sounds so much more emotively eye-catching than ordinary poverty. So may I be forgiven if I detect a whiff of the spin doctor about it? Has it emerged from that same Augean stable that shovelled out 'Ordinary Working People' and umpteen other meaningless phrases? I suppose that's the kind tosh that results from thinking that you can walk on water, or perhaps on a sea of

Dom Perignon, (providing it's paid for by someone else, of course). Regardless of whatever our political elite and their hangers-on may like to guzzle, even today 'The Dom' is still not the regular tipple of your 'ordinary working people'. But I guess that most spin doctors have forgotten what their archetypal working man even looks like, assuming they ever knew.

At my elementary or primary school in the second half of the 1930s there were some very poor children. I lived in a part of the Common in Horsham where some people struggled very hard to keep their heads above water. It was an accepted fact that the children of those families were poor because their parents were poor. There was no distinction between the parents and their children. I cannot believe that even in these callous times there are parents who will let the family starve while they live high in the hog themselves. So why bang on about *child* poverty? Why not just tackle poverty plain and simple, and let the rest follow? Can it be that politicians and reformers have been working at it for nearly 200 years – and that not even a wagonload of smart-asses could spin a 'story' out if that one.

Just a reminiscence about poor children. Poor little boys at my age mostly wore a kind of woolly shirt cum jumper with an integral collar and about three buttons at the neck. Freezing or sweltering, this was their wear for all seasons. Hankies were unheard of, and, as the kids spoke, two silver sacs of snot would dance from their nostrils, only to be called home by a prodigious sniff. But gravity would not be denied, and eventually these lively creatures would re-emerge from their nasal hideaways to execute an even more frenzied pas de deux, ever more daringly approaching the little boys' upper lip. Eventually a deft swipe of the hand would shatter their surface tension, and Mr and Mrs Snot would be scattered far and wide to leave only snail-like tracks over jumper, hands, walls and bystanders alike.

Poor little buggers. I wonder what kind of a life they have had and how they finished up. Not exactly overdone with the Dom Perignon, I fancy.

Talking of bargepoles in AD 1655

'Pray, tell me good sir, what is a bargepole?'

'Nay, sir, I know little of that thing, but I hear among the common folk 'tis much spoken of.'

'Dost thou then, in the vision of the mind, perchance, see there a punting pole?'

'Nay, sir, this I do know, a punt pole 'tis a lighter thing that now, on certain rivers, even wenches wield. (Yet, still on open water flat the noble punt the watery fowl with reeds and guns beguile into the hands of men, no work for Eve's weak kind.) Nay sir, the bargepole, so men say, is a weightier, longer tool, befitted only for the likes of Adam's sons, and them alone. 'Tis God's good gift to them, that cannot be denied.'

'And no one should deny it. What God hath granted Man no earthly power shall move. But, tell me, sir, these men with bargepoles great, how use they them, how bend they them to serve the Lord?'

'Why, sir, in very name their purpose lies. Those vessels on the rivers, barges called, at certain points of narrowness do cluster mightily, and men must poke with poles till they be freed from durance vile that holds them back. And then they onward sail, sometimes as far as Neptune's realm itself.'

'But men and women, whose hands have held them not, speak oft of bargepoles, and how they will with bargepoles nothing touch, so far from human kind vile things should ever be.'

'Aye, it is true, and may those things in Satan's realm for ever rest. Yet since the world began, that index of those things that bargepoles may not touch has grown and grown, and now by far o'ertops the evils of Pandora's box, which, ancients thought was shut but now return to plague all men, good Christians, Jew, the Infidel, and Turk alike.'

'And yet methinks so many evils do abound that bargepoles are too few, and times cry out as well for use of shortened sticks to keep at bay those evils, and then, when men descry old Satan's work, they all with one accord may cry, 'I shall have none of it, and neither with a bargepole nor short stick shall kith or kin of mine be seen to touch those loathsome things'.

OK, SO IT'S BARGEPOLES **AND** SHORT STICKS THEN.

Talking Sussex – Part One

Years ago, when I was a teenager – so it just has to be a long time ago – my parents and I knew a forerunner of Hyacinth Bucket (pronounced *boo-kay*). This lady lived with her husband, whose first name also happened to be Richard, at Welling, then always said to be in the County of Kent, but probably nowadays just lumped-in indiscriminately with 'South-east London'. Part of the household was a Staffordshire bull terrier bitch, which was almost as scary as her mistress. On walking this beast in Danson Park it had to be muzzled, otherwise it would annihilate other dogs and would open her jaws only after the prolonged application of lighted match to her nose. Although this creature was in perfect shape, her specific gravity was akin to Mike Tyson's after a prolonged diet of steak and eggs. Yet to human kind this Hound of the Baskervilles was fortunately a real softie, and liked nothing more than having her pink belly vacuumed with the cleaner attachment really meant for doing the curtains. (This is the only bitch I've known with this particular predilection. Perhaps I should have got out more.)

When we visited them for the first time, Hyacinth later confessed that before we arrived she wondered how the four-legged Frank Tyson would react to our 'Sussex voices'. Sussex voices? Well, that was a bit of a shock, since until then my mum and dad and I had no idea that our voices were any different from anyone else's. After all, we had crossed only one county boundary, from Sussex into Kent.

It's not as though we had blown in from Clydebank, or Truro, or Hartlepool or even Poplar. We had no idea that our voices were so overlaid with the rustic accents of the Sussex labouring poor that this may so incense even the dog that it would not rest until it had neatly laid out three bloody windpipes before her mistress. Maybe Hyacinth had imagined us arriving with Sussex clay adhering to our wellies, which we would then reluctantly wipe off using the straws we had plucked from our hair.

I could write volumes about Hyacinth and her long-suffering Richard. Although she was always bossing and embarrassing him, the fact was that he loved her. They say that people are loved for their weaknesses, not their strengths, for their vices not their virtues. Let's hope so. Anyway, the bull terrier finished up buried in their garden, and Hyacinth and Richard ended up sharing a grave in the cemetery. Needless to say, Richard died first, so Hyacinth, naturally enough, was still on top.

Talking Sussex – Part Two

Last time I wrote, I toyed with the idea of a bull terrier that might be able to recognize 'Sussex voices'. Assuming that a dog could do that fifty years ago, I wonder how many people could do it today? Or would they even be surprised to know that there was indeed a 'Sussex Dialect' with its own dictionary to help translate it?

It seems to me that a dialect has two components. One is the *way* things are said – the pronunciation and cadences –

and the other is the actual *words* and their meanings. We mostly recognize the regional differences from the way things are said, and you don't have to be *that* clever to spot the difference between the speech of a Norfolk Dumpling and a Scottish Haggis. Most actors are able to come up with a passable rendition of either, but after that they seem to fall back on the off-the-shelf lingo of 'Mummerset', an infectious condition easily picked up from the likes of Eddie or Joe Grundy.

But back to Sussex. Over the years, the recognizable sound of Sussex speech has been steadily diluted or extinguished by radio, education, travel and all those influences that turn a once-unchanging, rural fastness into part of the global village. The speech of the 'common man' in Sussex is no longer the sleepy drawl of the ploughman but the metropolitan patois of television entertainment. Even sixty years ago this wasn't so, and many old people of my acquaintance spoke with the authentic voices of their rustic forefathers.

The meaning of Sussex words, which required their own dictionary, is quite a different matter. Today hardly any of these words are common currency in Sussex speech, but in 1875 the Revd. W.D. Parish produced his famous (ie practically unknown) dictionary, the one and only from which any others are derived. Parish was the Vicar of Selmeston, a village between Lewes and Eastbourne, and, as far as I'm concerned, notable for its pub, the Barley Mow, a convenient stop for watering the horses on the way to the sea.

My copy of Parish's book is inscribed by the author, in a

neat scholarly hand – as one would expect of the careful researcher that he must have been. (Interesting how many bright Anglican clergymen gave their minds to study the new world of research and science, in between trotting round with the traditional bowls of soup for the deserving poor.) Sorry, but Part 3 of this particular bowl of soup will now have to cool down and wait – as we local yokels might say, 'till next *toim*'.

Talking Sussex – Part Three

You may recall that in Part Two we were commending the Revd. W. D. Parish on his *Dictionary of the Sussex Dialect* of 1875. Published by Farncombe of Lewes, just down the road from Selmeston where Parish was Vicar, the book is a nicely produced volume with hard covers in maroon cloth with gilt and blind die-stamping on the outside. I had always thought that the Dictionary was unique,A but in his acknowledgements Parish refers to a certain W. Durrant Cooper's *Sussex Glossary*. So evidently Parish wasn't the first in the field, and I guess that today a copy of Cooper's earlier book may be found only in a special library somewhere, if at all.

As often happens with desirable books that have gone out of copyright, we now have the benefit of a new version of the Dictionary. It has been re-issued by the Snake River Press of Alfriston, a rather arty outfit that specializes in little books about the County of Sussex.

The Snake River Press books are so well designed and

illustrated that they all shout loudly 'Buy Me!', an order that all 'Sussex nuts' or 'book nuts' are bound to obey at the double. And at £8-99 apiece they are remarkably good value, and you can check them out on the Snake River Press website.

Some of Parish's entries are fairly obvious, and others may not be confined to Sussex usage alone, but others are new (to me at least) and quite odd, so here's few to end with:

> BOZZLE: A confusion or mistake.
> BRONK: A distasteful toss of the head
> DOZZLE: A small quantity
> FORNICATE: To dawdle, waste time.
> GROUT-HEADED: Stupidly noisy
> HAITCH: A slight passing shower.
> HOGO : A strong foul smell.
> NUNTY: Dresssed in a shabby, old-fashioned way.
> SCALY: Inclined to steal.
> TRAMP: Gin and water

I hope that you've enjoyed fornicating with this dozzle of old Parish and that it hasn't driven you to resort to a tramp, at least before midday.

Tea *Alfresco*

Husband: OK, darling. I'm just off then. You doing anything special today?

Wife: Well, as it's a nice day and it's half-term I thought that the kids and I might take our tea down to the woods.

H: Good idea! No, hang on a minute. Maybe that's not such a good idea today of all days. As you're pregnant again, you don't want any big surprises.

W: Don't worry. The others always go down by the stream, and we'll stay well up the hill only on the edge of the woods. They won't trouble us.

H: Are you sure? You know they say you shouldn't go down there alone, might be better to stay at home altogether. Or even go in disguise.

W: Don't be silly, darling. I've never worn a disguise in my life! We shall be fine! That Rupert's really a sweetie, it's just his friends who look a bit odd.

H: Well, to tell the truth, it's that Steiff gang that worry me most. I reckon they've all got ASBOs. They didn't get those ear-tags for nothing!

W: But little Pooh is ok, he's nice and middle-class. His people take the *Telegraph*, like us. I know that for a fact, as the boy delivered theirs here once by mistake.

H: Well, it's an odd name. Just hope his personal hygiene is all it should be.

W: We won't get near enough to him for that to trouble us. Don't worry!

H: And I don't really like that family of three who always hang around with that cheeky blonde girl. Something fishy about that. Have you seen how the father looks at her? I'm sure he's damned well grooming her on the internet for *something*! Glad she's not my daughter! And the three are terrible sloppy eaters with food always spilt on their jumpers. They say it's porridge, but I bet it's cocaine. I wouldn't trust any of them. Even their kid looks sneaky.

W: No, darling, I'm sure they're harmless. Though I grant you the quiet one who looks like a tramp is a bit creepy – always expecting it to be wet. I've never seen him without that filthy old rain hat. They say he takes his own marmalade sandwiches everywhere. I do admit that's a bit weird.

H: Well, I shall worry about you all the time I'm at work. If you must go down to the woods today, just don't let the kids mix with them.

W: Well, darling it's not really *our* day today, it's really supposed to be *theirs*. And they're always dog tired by six, and then they get taken home to bed.

H: You're right, darling, as always. I'm certainly no snob. Live and let live say I. But just to please me – give them all a wide berth and make sure your mobile's fully charged, ok? Cheerio, Old Thing!

W: Bye-bye, darling. Do try to be home in time to see Bear Grylls.

The Crawler

I have been attending the Festival Theatre at Chichester since it opend in 1962, recently as a Festival 'Friend' and even more recently in a wheelchair. In 2012, before a performance of Shakespeare's Antony and Cleopatra, the lifts up to the wheelchair places broke down, and front-of-house staff deployed a mechanical 'stair crawler' to get me upstairs. So I thanked them in the spirit of the play which they had enabled me to see:

Lines on a Stair Crawler
A light-hearted thank-you to Matt, Chris and colleagues,
22/9/2012

Recalling how that warrior Enobarbus
So well described fair Cleopatra's throne,
To ferry back athwart the fateful Styx we paid
Grim-visaged Charon to bring that very soldier
Back to us, that he may then narrate to all
How Horsham John, no less than he, was brought
To scorn the lowly earth and sit along his lady Gail
And contemplate the players from Row 'L'.

And so, old Enobarbus spake:
'Since mother nature or some rebellious god
Had taken from old John that gift to move
One leg before the other, that common means whereby
Most men traverse the face of goodly earth,
Fair Providence had gifted John a cart,
Yet t'was a chariot, not drawn by steeds nor eunuchs
From Ethiop's far shore, but any men and dames
Of kind intent and sinews bold to match.
But even so, such valiance of muscles strong
Could not bring John and chariot and all
To mount those stairs whereby he might attain Row 'L'.

'And then, as though to us unheard a tucket sounded,
Four lusty swains in sable garb attired came forth,
And with them brought an engine strange,
The like no man had seen on land or sea before.
With Vulcan's bands they quickly clamped John's cart
To their device, it wheezing much, as doth the sow
When bringing forth her young, old John did
Mount the stair, and then the next, and then
The next one after, till all those stairs
Lay vanquished at the feet of John and burly swains.
And I, old Enobarbus, now rejoice that I came back,
Escaping Cerberus's deadly fangs so now that I may
Tell how Horsham John was lifted up to witness from
Row 'L' the doings of great Antony.'

The Feral Ferrule

Sometimes the dailies run one of those space-filling articles listing strange words culled from the dictionary, 'funny' words to amaze us. There are plenty of them. Sometimes 'wayzgoose' makes an appearance because from time to time someone takes it out of the reserve collection, dusts it down and puts it on show solely to flabbergast. 'What an *odd* word,' we say. Then back it goes again until its next airing. During my daily round I have never needed to refer to a printing firm's annual junket, which is what a wayzgoose is. No doubt printers still have works outings, but I bet that nowadays they are a darned sight more sophisticated than that lovely home-spun word seems to imply. Can't you just imagine in 1950-

something about a dozen blokes, all collared and tied and smelling of ink and Wrights Coal Tar soap, setting off from a small printing shop in, say, Glastonbury, for a sedate day by the sea at Weymouth?

One of the words recently cited as a bit of an oddball is 'ferrule', which is so common that its inclusion seems quite baffling, and would surely score a big fat zero on the scale of verbal gobsmackers. Who doesn't know that this f-word is the metal tip of an umbrella, with echoes of that infamous killer prick marinated in ricin? At least, that was the definition the paper dished up. But my guess is that most older readers will think 'rubber' first, and 'metal' a long way behind, because those blobs at the end of my crutches are also ferrules, and etymologically confusing though it may be, I would hate them to be crafted from anything but the finest latex, and I guess I'm not alone in becoming a self-taught expert on that lively beast, the ferrule.

We who lean heavily on crutches or sticks – (the American 'cane' sounds so weedy that I wouldn't even take one for a test-drive) – know full well that ferrules must always understand who's boss. Once planted on terra firma they must stay put, because if they wander it's a dead cert that you will wander too, and in no time you will be treated to close-up view of the floor or the pavement. And in getting down there you will realize that you can move a damned sight quicker vertically than you can horizontally.

No, choose a well-bred chunky rubber ferrule and be kind to it. Don't let it wear itself out in your service, and never plonk it down carelessly on wet York pavings or soggy sycamore leaves. Because if you do, it will bare its fangs and turn positively feral. 'The metal tip of an umbrella'? Is that *really* all it is? Brother, believe me, you don't know the half of it. Give me a good fat rubber ferrule every time. I'd even take it with me on a wayzgoose to Weymouth.

The Man in Plum Corduroys

The year was 1956, the month probably September. A venerable Austin saloon trundled to a stop outside a secondhand and antiquarian bookshop recently opened in Arundel and three elderly gents alighted. The bookshop owner noticeably deferred to one of the passengers, a portly figure wearing a striking pair of plum-coloured corduroy trousers. Behind one of the bookcases and taking in the scene was a young(er) John Snelling witnessing for the first and last time the arrival of one Philip Hugh Padwick of Fittleworth, who as far back as 1901 had described himself in the census for that year as an 'Artist Painter'. Although Philip Padwick was now living at Tripp Hill, Fittleworth, his ancestry was rooted in Horsham and his elder brother, John, sat on the Horsham bench and was living in the town at 29, North Street. This was a double-fronted Georgian town house right on the pavement with a Victorian addition at its north end. Its glory was its gardens, full of fine shrubs, which stretched far back to border on the boundary of Horsham Park. Where is it all now? Well, after John Padwick died in 1957 the house and gardens fell to the bulldozers and the tower block that became the first Sun Alliance building rose up in their place.

Not long after Philip's death in 1958 that same fellow, who from the behind the bookcases had witnessed Padwick's arrival at the shop, received one of his paintings as a gift, an event that has led to a voyage of discovery around this artist's long career. Padwick has been called an impressionist, but it's hard to justify that name. Some of his earlier paintings are more reminiscent of the Baroque French painter Claude Lorrain, but always at the centre has been his affection for Sussex and in particular the valley of the River Arun. It appears that most of his paintings could have been inspired by landscapes no more than ten miles or so from his own front door. More and more he concentrated on the beloved river, the water meadows and the Downs, and some works look so similar to others that one suspects that he just turned his easel a few degrees and started to paint almost the same scene all over again. Perhaps he was following the precedent of John Linnell a century before him, who was quite content to knock out replicas of paintings that had rung the public's bell.

According to the website *Your Paintings* no less than fourteen public galleries in Britain possess paintings by Padwick. Brighton and Hove Museum and Art Gallery lead the field with nine, and Worthing has five. We in Horsham have three in the Museum, but others are scattered from Newport to Scotland's National Trust Brodie Castle. One wonders how many are currently on view and how many are tucked away unseen in the so-called 'reserve collections'.

One suspects that over time Padwick's style has fallen a bit out of favour and his oils can now usually be bought at auction for anything between £50 and £150 depending on size – better value than mere reproductions of some more contemporary artists. Anyway, three cheers for old Padwick, who back in 1956 aged 80 wasn't afraid to be seen in Arundel wearing plum-coloured pants!

The Nerd's Tale

I've been collecting Beltz porcelain for some time. The Beltz factory, close to Leipzig, flourished at the same time as Meissen, but has always been somewhat overshadowed by its more famous neighbour. Their modeller, Hans Goetz, was as skilled as Kaendler, but, being less known, his work today fetches less money. Leafing through an art magazine one day I found a display cabinet that would have suited my collection perfectly, so I ordered it. After it had twice been delivered to the wrong house, then left on my doorstep in the rain, I invited a friend to help me unpack it all and to assemble it. Since one corner of the box had evidently been run over by a fork-truck, we were relieved to find nothing damaged. Also, imprints of heavy boots on the box had not affected its contents.

The instructions for assembly were in Chinese, and the maker had forgotten to enclose his American version. The rodwell boards had been nicely faced in fawley wood, with the ends reinforced with cobant alloy to simulate ormolu. Strength was given to the structure by fashioning the retaining gleats from fibreglass and securing them to the rodwell boards by slotting brass mogle wedges into pre-cut slots. Unfortunately the position of the slots did not coincide with the wedges. It was lucky that the billy-flashings were made of light plastic, so between us we were able to bend them sufficiently to get nine of the twenty-six wedges to match up with the slots. The whole unit was designed to be secured to the wall by a series of overlapping rove brackets. Of the screws found in a small bag, half had tops with little crosses, while the others had flat heads. My friend said the latter were nails. As the walls of my property are very hard, we had to drill the wall using masonry bits, two of which broke, one catching my friend's ear and he ended up sprinkling one of the fawley wood facings with his blood. We finished the job in the early hours, and I rejoiced when the long-awaited moment came to begin to display my Beltz pieces. Some of the taller figures were too big for the unit, so had to stand along the top shelf. It all looked great, and well worth the trouble. Sadly, during the night the whole unit came off the wall and every piece of Beltz was damaged in one way or another. As we all know, a piece of damaged Beltz, or Meissen for that matter, is hardly worth having. My theory is that during the night the billy-flashings, which we had bent to fit, had sprung back and so suddenly withdrawn the mogles from their slots, with disastrous consequences. The most worrying thing of all is how the makers of the unit were allowed to use fawley wood in their product, as it is, as all the world knows, a very rare and endangered species of hardwood.

My friend has tried repeatedly to contact David Attenborough on the subject but without success, so is now getting up a petition to the Dalai Lama.

Titfers

Once upon a time the slogan 'If you want to get ahead get a hat' was as well known as Fay Weldon's 'Go to work on an egg'. Well, it takes more than a snappy phrase to stem the relentless tide of fashion, and if the beleaguered hat-makers of Britain were trying to turn defeat into a victory then someone should have told them that however long they waited on the beach at Dunkirk there would never be a flotilla of rescue ships appearing over the horizon to the echo of chords by Elgar or Walton. And it's all happened relatively quickly.

When I worked in the City of London for a short time, well, EC4 actually which is more Fleet Street than the City proper, my bus went through a then rather run-own stretch of Stamford Street which included a grimy house announcing that it had once been the manufactory of *Tress the Hatters*. I always imagined this place once peopled by Dickensian characters like Bob Cratchett or Smike working a twelve-hour day in darkly horrible conditions turning out silk hats and bowlers for the great and the good.

My guess is that in the year that I was born a few grandees were still sporting toppers when they were up and dressed or attending a cabinet meeting. (An old newsreel soundtrack pronounces it *cabinay*.) In a demented moment invested in a bowler hat and actually wore it in London a few times, entirely oblivious to what a complete prat I must have looked. Yet thanks to the kindness of strangers nobody pursued me down the street with catcalls.

Thanks to a late and dear member of my Rotary Club, I now regularly wear a baseball cap and have several of them. It seemed that if my friend, who was both a scholar and a gentleman, could wear one, then that was good enough for yours truly. Though he maintained that donning this particular headgear at once reduces the wearer's IQ by 10%, and back to front reduces it by 20%. I have worn my Yankees cap in New York, and a blue one sporting the word 'Canada' in Vancouver. But I've never worn the Canada cap south of the 49TH Parallel. My IQ may have been seriously impaired, but I'm not that stupid.

Up The Garden Path

Anyone ever heard of Thomas Edward Brown? With a name like that very probably. He could be anyone's grandfather or a bloke down the pub, but the one we have in mind was born in 1830 and was responsible for

A garden is a lovesome
Thing, God wot!
Rose plot,
Fern'd grot-...

This epic sneaked its way into the *Oxford Book of English Verse* when the anthology first appeared in 1900, and has remained a favourite aunt sally for, among other things, his 'God wot', an antique version of 'God knows', and God only wot why he wrote it that way. Anyway, the editor selected the poem again for inclusion in his *Oxford Book of Victorian Verse* which appeared in 1912. Actually, old Brown was quite an interesting chap. To begin with, he was born on the Isle of Man and spent much of his life there, and you don't see too many three-legged poets around.

Leaving aside his 'God wotting', it seems that some of his poetry is not at all bad, though it would be hard to tell as much of it he wrote in the Anglo-Manx dialect. A rather good quip of his was 'The joke of a rich man is always funny'. No doubt he was a bright boy, and went from Man to Oxford as a 'servitor' at Christ Church, a position that allowed him to be educated more or less for nothing in return for acting as a dogsbody to the college fellows. He finished up with a double first and became a fellow of Oriel College, but the Dean there later blocked his appointment as a senior professor on the grounds that low-life like a former servitor had never held that position before! No wonder his crack about rich men's jokes bore more than a trace of cynicism. This, of course, was in the days when 'social mobility' was to be feared slightly more than the plague.

Unsurprisingly he escaped from Oxford and later became a master at the newly-founded Clifton College near Bristol which is still going strong. There he stayed for nigh on thirty years, apparently much loved and respected by everyone, retiring finally to his beloved Isle of Man. So there was clearly a bit more to old Thomas Edward Brown than his 'God wot', 'rose plot' and 'fern'd grot' might lead us to believe. At least, the Manx TT Races won't disturb his slumbers, as he finished up next to his wife at Redland Parish Church back in Bristol.

Voices

According to G. B. Shaw, one of his reasons for writing *Saint Joan* was to 'save her from John Drinkwater'. Hands up, those who have ever seen a play by John Drinkwater? It's as though both of them have now been whirling around in that unforgiving washing machine of Time a little too long and both have emerged proportionately shrunken. The one person who hasn't shrunk, of course, is Joan herself. As *The Sun* might say, 'it was the Church what burnt her', so it was to be expected that, given time, the Church would take it all back and make her a saint.

History and G.B.S. are at one in picking up on the fact that the maid from Domrémy was prompted to do all the things that she did because her 'voices' told her to. If her voices had told her to find her way to the nearest convent and spend her life keeping bees or washing the sisters' undies, then the chances are we would never have heard another peep out of her. But Joan's voices sounded decidedly militant, urging her to don armour, take up the sword, and throw the English out of La France. So off she went, booted and spurred to ensure herself a place in history, well, French history anyway. The English left France eventually, but who can say whether Joan had much to do with it?

What is of lasting interest is the phenomenon of people being told to do things by voices that they can hear but no one else can. Apparently, this didn't stop with St. Joan, and according to the Internet it goes on all the time. At the other end of the spectrum it's on record that people who are seriously disturbed in the head sometimes hear a voice telling them to go out and do something really awful. And sometimes they go out and do something really awful.

My guess is that many of the 'voices' people hear actually come not from their hearts or heads but from rather lower down, from their own innards. It's commonly known as a 'rumbling tummy' but has the medical name *borborygmus*. Between sleeping and waking these murmurings can at times sound remarkably lifelike. In an adolescent girl, all psyched up as Joan was, I bet her guts were always working overtime, and her butterflies were more like fruit bats swooping around inside her and kicking up a dreadful racket. Poor kid. Shame it all had to end the way it did, sainthood notwithstanding.

Be sure that before the next Grand National I shall have a supper of strong cheese and pickled onions, and if after that I don't hear the name of the first past the post loud and clear, I shall retire to the nearest monastery and keep bees.

'Whence comes that goodly fragrance…?'

A few years ago I made my first (and only) visit to New York, and the itinerary, of course, just had to include an assault on Fifth Avenue. Spinning in and out of St. Patrick's Cathedral and the shops on a three-wheeled scooter was great fun, and managing to whizz up and down in Tiffany's without spending a dime made an old man very happy – and there are precious few ways of doing that. But when it came to Saks, a token purchase seemed obligatory, so wheeling around the perfumery boutiques on the ground floor we came out with a bottle of aftershave masquerading as eau de toilette, for monsieur, naturally. It was called *Mania* from Giorgio Armani. One never ceases to wonder why on earth Armani went to the Medical Dictionary to find a name for it, and not a very nice one at that. How long before we get *Cystitis* from Chanel, or *Haemorrhoids pour Hommes*? But thinking about it, this practice is not new. A few years earlier Calvin Klein had called one of their products *Obsession*, which really means the same as *mania*. Going back a bit further, Dior made a big hit with the perfume, *Poison*, and in the later 1980s our ladies looked as lovely as ever but had a whiff of *Lucrezia Borgia* about them.

All this has reminded us of a phrase that was common when I was a lad, but now is never heard. It's *religious mania*. It would be interesting to know when and how this expression came into common currency. Going back to mediaeval Christendom the constant fear of everlasting damnation must have turned most of Europe and half of Asia into entire continents of 'religious maniacs'. One suspects that we have worked through the period of history when the phrase had any meaning. And now we have moved even further and what once was designated mania of the religious sort is now better understood and classified as, say, Islamist Extremism, Christian Fundamentalism, Jehovah's Witnessism, Communism, Fascism, stamp collecting. Come to that, doesn't every religion demand of its followers some degree of mania, otherwise those without it are labelled back-sliders or infidels? So now when the dentist asks me if I needs a painkilling injection, the answer is always, 'Yes, for religious reasons. I'm a devout coward. In fact, as far as painkillers are concerned I'm a right religious maniac.' And what's more, i now has the aftershave to prove it!

Who do you think you are?

'Who do you think you are?' The words could be the overture for a fight or a casual stabbing, but the square-eyed will recognize the title of a tv programme tracing the ancestry of well-known people. (I say 'well-known', but as usual have to add that a good half of today's 'well-known' I've never heard of. And I'm pretty sure they've never heard of me, either, so that makes us quits.)

I've seen three programmes so far, and only the *enfant terrible* Boris J. managed to keep his lachrymal ducts under control. The other two put up the briefest of struggles before irrigating their environment *con brio*. Well, one shouldn't be too quick to take the mick. The same thing has happened to me, and it's music that does it. And it's nearly always something by Edward Elgar. It happened again on a flight to New York. It was my reaction to his First Symphony on my headphones that caused a flight attendant to enquire if I was all right. (Sometimes one gets tired of words, and only music that mainlines straight to the soul will do.)

In the case of the weeping celebrities – how's that for a Sherlock Holmes title? – what turned on their stopcocks was finding out what a rough time their forebears had had. Well, I guess we could all do that, as I'm sure that few of our ancestors had it easy. Even so, they struggled on, living kindly, decent lives, and going to their unmarked graves without stabbing anyone or vandalizing any thing. No, the most memorable feature of 'Who Do You Think...' is the amazing archival records that the genealogists manage to turn up. The trail leads to some one-eyed town somewhere in Europe, or even the UK, and there on hand in some back-street town hall, library or church vestry is the expert, white gloves at the ready, producing ledgers and files two or three hundred years old to answer the celebs' questions.

Generations of conscientious scribes have spent their lives in laboriously recording the minutiae of the world around them – birth, marriage, death, commerce, property, they're all there, perhaps lying in an antiquated strongbox, or, more likely, now occupying a shelf in miles of air-conditioned racks that silently glide on runners at the touch of a wheel. They represent millions of man hours of pens being put to paper down the centuries.

Are the great days of careful archiving now over? Are we now into the age of the disc and the memory stick? And how long will they last? Five years? Ten years? And if some clot loses a memory stick while engrossed in the pole-dancing, then we're talking not centuries, or years, but minutes. Anyway, we can be sure that some bone-head will pop up and chant the usual mantra, 'Lessons have been learnt, lessons have been learnt... lessons...' 'Oh shut it!'

Apologia
– a memoir–

Introduction

I am what could be called 'a cradle Anglican', born into, and brought up as a member of, the Church of England. Now, at the end of a long lifetime, I am interested to note how the Church of England and my own attitude towards it have changed over the years. But this needs a context, and that context is my own life story. So bit by bit I found the life story rather taking over, so that unintentionally I have woven a kind of autobiography, but one generously embroidered with 'religious' threads.

The title, *Apologia*, pays impertinent homage to Newman's *Apologia Pro Vita Sua*, and perhaps might therefore also earn it the subtitle of *Folie de Grandeur*. A further subtitle might be *Standing Back*, since the whole of life seems to be always progressively 'standing back' in order to get a wider view. At least the biography is <u>mine</u> and no one else's, so therefore it is unique. But you have no need to remind me that uniqueness in itself confers neither value nor significance.

Ab ovo

As I am English and born over eighty-five years ago, the first words that I learnt by heart was *The Lord's Prayer*, to be recited in pyjamas kneeling beside a small single bed. The pyjamas normally lived in the belly of a cute furry black and white terrier and were released nightly by a caesarian zip. (The bed itself was one move up from a wooden cot with bars and a drop-side that made a satisfying rattle when shaken by little hands.) No doubt at that time most of my contemporaries would have learnt that same prayer, which would stay with them until maybe the moment came for them to say it, or to have it said over them, perhaps at the time of their death. At the cot stage, to encourage sleep my mother would sing a song, 'Whose little baby are you?', which much later research on my part revealed that she had adapted her lullaby from a Jerome Kern musical staged in New York in 1920.

When I was born it was taken for granted that everyone was Christian because it was like the air we all breathed and was taken for granted without thinking about it. Everyone was either nominally 'Church of England', 'Chapel' (ie Non-Conformist), or 'Roman Catholic'. We did not know that there were such things as other religions but we learnt that there was an amorphous mass of 'heathens' overseas ('in distant lands afar thick darkness broodeth yet') and it was the job of the churches to turn them into Christians by the efforts of the missionaries sent out from the mother country to proselytize through education and general beneficence and so disperse that thick darkness. In many a house there were 'missionary boxes' to collect the householder's loose coins, to be picked up and emptied regularly by someone from the church. My mother's mother had two boxes in her bureau, one marked *The Church Missionary Society* and the other *Waifs and Strays*, not an animal charity but one for very poor people, of whom there were plenty. By the end of secondary schooling we might have learnt that outside these classifications there were a few people who, in spite of knowing about religion, preferred not to have a religion at all and that these people were either agnostics or atheists, though they were clearly eccentric and either probably 'not all there' or 'too clever by half'. We didn't know any of them personally.

My father and mother were both born in the north-west Sussex town of Horsham in 1905 and 1904 respectively. As far as I can tell, all the ancestors from way back were also Sussex born. My mother was brought up within the Church of England. Her father, John, who was born in Billingshust, was a stonemason and had helped to build the church that the family thereafter attended, Holy Trinity in Horsham, which is one of the parish's daughter churches. John later became a 'sidesman' at the church, (a kind of front of house helper), and my mother taught at the Sunday school there until I was expected, so I reckon that I have attended there *ab ovo*. On my father's side, thanks to the zeal of his grand-father, my paternal grandparents and my father were brought up within the milieu of a strict Baptist chapel, and, once my father had escaped from the rigours of three compulsory services every Sunday plus patriarchal Bible readings at home, he rather felt that he had had enough 'religion' to last him a lifetime, though he always remained benevolent towards the churches and their clergy. Without shouting about it his entire, good and blameless life was imbued and motivated by Christian mores. Many people in

The Common area of Horsham where we lived instinctively turned to him for help in time of trouble. Holy Trinity Church has memorials to the dead of both wars. As it happens, my grandfather carved the names on the first one and my father those on the second.

I never knew my paternal grandfather, who also happened to be a stonemason, because he died of a brain tumour in 1915 when my father was only ten, but my father did recall seeing him laying the lovely chess-board floor in the St. John chapel of St. Mary's, Horsham's parish church. (Coincidentally, work by my own father may also be seen in that church.)

My parents enjoyed reading and a current volume could always be found on the bedside table of each of them. As a child I made frequent visits with my mother to the Horsham Library, then housed in the old St. Mark's Church hall, or to the subscription library upstairs in Boots. I shall never forget the smell of the old library in St. Mark's Hall. I don't know how or why, but my parents also had a taste for art. Early in their married life they regularly bought an art magazine that gave away coloured prints some of which my father framed himself. These they hung in their little house so they are part of my earliest memories. There was Gainsborough's *Blue Boy* and at the top of the stairs Reynolds's *Age of Innocence*, a young girl who always frightened me a little as from a distance her voluminous dress resembled the head of a camel-like creature. Finally, there was G.F. Watts's *Hope*, even then a strangely sombre choice for a young married couple in 1929. (Only recently I discovered that what I always thought was a rickety chair in the Watts painting is really a lyre with broken strings – which certainly gives more point to the title.) I feel that the wheel has turned a full circle because once I owned an original Watts drawing myself.

When I was about five years old removing children's tonsils and adenoids almost seemed a rite of passage. They suggested it for me, but as my parents wished to spare me my first hospital experience the operation was to be done at home. I vividly remember the day. A large Pembroke table that was only brought in at Christmas was duly found and dusted down and placed in the biggest bedroom beneath the window and towels laid out on it. At 10 am the surgeon and anaesthetist drove themselves up in separate cars and remained in their ordinary day clothes. The anaesthetist was my mother's (and my) GP, Dr Alice Owen. The surgeon was Dr Geoffrey Sparrow, famed as a hunting man, artist and writer. I think that he probably held a torch to see down my throat. The anaesthetic was a gauze pad sprinkled with chloroform from a medicine bottle and held over my nose and mouth. I don't remember a nurse or anyone else being there. When I came out of the anaesthetic around 4 o'clock that afternoon the doctors had long since gone. But earlier on when my father looked into the room he was a bit shaken to see me snoring loudly on a bed of bloody towels. For some nights afterwards I was kept awake by earache and pains in the neck. But my reward for it all was a Hornby train set and a torch that would produce white, red and green lights. Much later I was told that my tonsils had grown back again.

Both my parents had got along well with the Vicar of Horsham (inducted in 1934), one Canon R.W.D. Lee, a Mirfield trained Yorkshireman whose saturnine expression belied a lively humour and kindly nature. Sometimes he would stroll into the masonry workshop for a chat and always be welcome there. This raises an interesting issue concerning how the laity responded to the clergy in those days. A universal accolade appeared to be 'he doesn't seem to be like a clergyman'. Does this reveal that ministers of religion had a shocking reputation, so that not to appear like one was a compliment? (By a strange coincidence, Lee's son Martin went up to Trinity the year I went up to Fitzwilliam, and though I knew who he was I felt much too insignificant to introduce myself.)

During quiet periods of the Second World War I would trot along Trafalgar Road on a Sunday afternoon to attend Sunday School in church. (One of the teachers was a genteel Kate Orwin, whose cousin was naval war hero, Philip Vian.) My mother was a fairly regular communicant at the Sunday 8am service, and, as I lay in bed, I could always recognize her footsteps as she came down the road and home to get the breakfasts. I did not join her at Holy Communion of course until I had been confirmed, which was after I had gone to Collyer's, the grammar school for boys. My confirmation class was held at the school, mainly by the Headmaster, Philip A. Tharp, and some by Canon Lee. Tharp is reckoned to be one of the 'great headmasters', in the tradition of so many grammar and public schools. He really deserves a chapter to himself, though maybe today's educational world would give him short shrift, beating miscreant boys as he did probably on a daily basis and encouraging the school's prefects to do the same. The induction ceremony of a new prefect was to be beaten by all the other prefects in turn. When I became a prefect myself I believe that I was let off quite lightly, but I still ended up with a backside that would not have shamed one of Attenborough's baboons. Tharp was well-liked and certainly respected by most of his past pupils. Some of my own more personal strictures on 'P.A.T.' or 'The Old Man' might be considered harsh, but the intellectual rigour of his school and its harvest of Oxbridge scholarships are beyond question. But he was a captive of the ideas of his own era and stratum of society, as most of us are. By 'stratum of society', of course, I mean *class*, a word so generously endowed with irrelevant association that it is best avoided.

I tried for open scholarships at Oxford and Cambridge, the first one at Wadham College. The exams were held in the college's beautiful hall under its great hammer-beam roof. As it was a cold week in March, frosting the crocuses on the quad lawn, the supervising don, (one Dr. Bamborough?), kept throwing logs on to the fire, which just smoked and produced no warmth. At the end of three hours we left the hall cold but well kippered. In addition, the great sash window of my room in the eighteenth century building that fronts Parks Road was permanently stuck wide open and I could not budge it. So my memories of Oxford were not of the warmest. (In later years I saw Oxford from a different perspective after being a dinner guest at St. Catherine's High Table during the mastership of Dr Alan, later Lord, Bullock.)

I fared little better at the December scholarship exams at Cambridge. Here I was at Queens' College in an old room near the gatehouse, pervaded by urinal disinfectant that rose from below stairs. (This had been Tharp's college.) Again, it was cold, with a fine, hard sleet like rice, blowing horizontally and appropriately from the east. How often was I told that there is nothing standing between Russia and Cambridge?

My mother and I did sometimes attend the early communion service or evensong. We did this on the October Sunday before I went up to Cambridge the next day on an eventual state scholarship to read English at Fitzwilliam House (later Fitzwilliam College). At the start of the autumn term of 1951 I felt that things would change and never be the same again. They did and they weren't.

Going up
The elation that I and the family felt at my 'going to Cambridge' knew no bounds. Had he lived, my grandfather John Gumbrill would have been delighted, as 'little John' was the apple of his eye. In his will he left me two houses, but not having second sight I sold them to their tenants for less than a thousand pounds for the two of them. (Their current value must be around half a million.) '*Stupid boy!*' No one in the whole family had ever entered a university before. But I was not the last. A few years later my cousin

Michael followed me from Collyer's School on a scholarship to Queens' Cambridge and laid the foundation of a most distinguished academic career as Head of Science and house master at the public school, Harrow.

The war had ended only six years before I arrived at Cambridge, and food rationing was still in force and in many parts of the country bomb damage remained evident. At night as I walked beneath the street lights in Trumpington Street my begowned shadow walked before me, a sight that never failed to delight me. I was actually at Cambridge, wearing the undergraduate gown! As we would say today, 'WOW!'

The lectures at the Mill Lane theatres were a constant pleasure. The lecturers were clever, eccentric, urbane, funny, some of them the authors of the literary criticism that I was reading at the time – E.M.W. Tillyard, F.R. Leavis, George Rylands, David Daiches. Only an idiot would wish to play truant from their lectures. A Saturday morning bonus was the opportunity to hear Nikolaus Pevsner talking on art, and using a huge and ancient epidiascope to project his pictures.

But to return to the 'religious' thread, which is meant to provide a recurring theme for this memoir and to justify borrowing John Henry Newman's title. At Cambridge I did not warm to the college chaplain, who in a one-to-one quite soon urged me to kneel and pray that I should soon see the light. I was instantly put off by the bright-eyed evangelists of the Cambridge Inter-collegiate Christian Union, (Kick-you for short), who were eager for me to be 'saved' just as they had been. That kind of talk just made me uncomfortable and gnawed at my self-confidence. So I tended to gravitate to the University Church of Great St. Mary for evensong with an appealing vicar, good singing and a relaxed style to which I was more accustomed at home.

In my second year at Cambridge I was joined by a close school friend, Brian Masters. Because of our friendship our respective parents also became friends and the families remained so until death eliminated all four of them decades later. Although I could write at length about Brian Masters, sufficient to say here that in 1998 he died prematurely as Bishop of Edmonton in the London Diocese. As a youth he said that he thought that he would either enter the church or politics. As it happens, he did both simultaneously. (More on Bishop Brian follows this memoir in *Apologia Plus*.)

Unlike my own family, Brian's was entirely unsullied by any knowledge of the church or any interest in it, but I guess that while on National Service he had been 'got at' by some unknown Army chaplain and by the time he reached Cambridge, aided and abetted by his college, he was ready to be confirmed. The service occurred at Ely Cathedral during his first term and was taken by its bishop, the saintly-looking Dr Edward Wynn. This was the first time that I ever saw a bishop dispensing benedictions to right and left as he sailed slowly down the aisle in procession. Until then I had witnessed only the Pope do that on film or television.

This piece of Catholic ritual chimed well with Brian's inclinations, and in no time on Sundays he and I found ourselves regularly attending two of Cambridge's high

Anglican churches, St. Mary the Less and St. Bene't's. The main service at St. Mary's was high mass, conducted by priest, deacon and sub-deacon suitably attired in the appropriate Eucharistic vestments and wearing birettas. Clergy and acolytes always faced the altar looking eastward, so the congregation had a rear view of the choreographed movement of white surplices and richly embroidered vestments. An evident fashion of the time was for the priest to speak so quickly that his prayers were almost gabbled, as though he could not wait for it all to be over. The expert at this was the American priest, Father Casey. Eerily surging music from an unseen organ would underline the mystery of the proceedings. By the end of the service a fog of incense had enveloped everyone and was still clinging to our clothes while later we drank a post-service glass of sherry in the lounge of *The Blue Boar* in Trinity Street. Any passer-by with a nose could tell exactly where we had spent the morning. Because the rule was to fast before taking Holy Communion, at a mid-morning service it was expected that most people would have already eaten breakfast, so only the old or sick would be expected to receive the communion elements. Usually one or two Miss Havisham figures, clothed in black rather than white, would venture from their seats to make their precarious journey up the aisle to reach the welcome support of the altar rail. This tradition of fasting for later services has been abandoned long since, of course.

At this time the vicar at the ancient St. Ben'et's Church, which is nearer the city centre, was a priest of the Anglican

Franciscan Order, Father Lothian Sumner, and this was the place to go for an early (1662 said) service of Holy Communion, and to partake in it. This service contrasted starkly with the Little St. Mary's High Mass, being a low-key and quiet affair. Sometimes the server at the altar would be a Dr Geoffrey Bushnell, an archaeologist who occasionally appeared before a wider congregation on a popular television programme.

Personally, I found the general ambience of these churches more to my liking. It was relaxed and related strongly to the beauty of words and music and colour, with no one badgering to know the current state of health of one's immortal soul. I have written elsewhere how at Little St. Mary's the clergy would quickly disrobe and race to the church porch to say goodbye and to be drawing deeply on their first post-communion cigarettes. The scene could have been written by Evelyn Waugh.

I believe that somewhere in *Brideshead* Waugh's character warns that at Oxford most high Anglican men are 'sodomites', or words to that effect. I was for a long time lamentably uninstructed about this area of life, but was aware that there was an effeminacy about some men, as there had been a 'girlishness' about some boys at school. I was never sure exactly what they 'did' to make them different, an ignorance that today is surely replicated nowhere on this earth. No one will need a review of the social history of the last fifty years to illustrate the changes. At this time, of course, homosexual behaviour was illegal and it is fair to say rather looked down upon by the majority of people, except by that secret cadre of the initiated who apparently, completely unknown to me, had always existed and were drawn from every stratum of society.

On one occasion at Cambridge I did pick up some vibrations of this in the high church. It was allegedly a party, though even for those austere days it was pretty thin gruel. It was a gathering of mostly men in a college room. At the door was a cardinal's scarlet biretta flanked by two lighted candles, a daring and pertly flirtatious reference to the Church of Rome. I imagine that people took a bottle of wine of some sort, and there must have been a little food. Yes, there were a few biscuits. A few of the people there I knew by sight but some others attended another high Anglican church at the other end of town and I knew none of them. The main purpose of the party seemed to be just talk, and if there was another agenda then I knew nothing of it. There were a couple of clergy, probably the only ones there. One of them I recognized as a prominent figure in the University and the other apparently was the vicar of that church at the other end of town. I suppose the partygoers could be described as slightly camp, though at the time that was not a word in my vocabulary. One of the undergraduates was dressed as a nun or a friar, in a brown habit anyway, and at one stage the nun was sitting on the knee of the prominent churchman. (Years later the unhappiness of this poor cleric was revealed to the world when he spectacularly destroyed himself in the heart of Cambridge. I note from his biography in Wikipedia that his death is not described, so who am I to say more?) I was feeling rather out of my depth here and uneasy about all this and decided it was time for me to leave, a decision reinforced when a photographer appeared. (Maybe I had the instinct of a politician without actually being one.) The same thought had occurred to the 'other' cleric, who went for his coat at the same time as I did. 'Oh, do you have to go, Father?' I enquired innocently. He mumbled a reply and I thought, 'Yes, you know which side your bread is buttered you cunning old fox and it's not by appearing in the *Cambridge Daily News* photographed in this company'.

High Church Anglicans celebrate the execution of King Charles I on 31st January 1649, in the belief that Charles was martyred in defence the true, Episcopal faith of the Church of England. On the day Brian and I attended a commemoration service; it must have been in January 1953. Looking back on it, we were a quaint looking lot, with a scattering of college clergy suitably biretta-ed and robed to conduct a service on a Saturday morning in a chilly St. Edward's Church in the town centre. An earnest Franciscan brother present heard that there was a painting of King Charles somewhere around, whereupon the brother enquired seriously, 'Is it within venerating distance?' Brian and I had not lost our sense of the ridiculous and tried hard not to laugh at the incongruity of the holy man's question. (What is the standard venerating distance for royal ikons? Be sure, there will be a paper on exactly that subject somewhere in the University or the Bodleian Library.)

One of my first acts at Cambridge was to join the historic Union Society as a life member. It cost me, (ie my father), seven and a half guineas. It's President then was the patrician Douglas Hurd, who was destined to become our Foreign Secretary, and it was he who showed the new members around. A later President was Greville Janner, and although I never knew Janner personally I have always found it hard to believe that he was, or later turned into, a sexual predator of boys and men. Other Union big shots at that time were Nicholas Tomalin and Brian Redhead. The Oxford and Cambridge Union Societies are both ancient debating societies and are far removed from the student union movement at what today is often known as 'uni', a somewhat demeaning slang term for a university. (I will never, never, never refer to Cambridge as 'uni', Ugh!) At home I had been a member of the Young Conservatives as in the family Conservatism was a 'default position' rather like our Anglican Christianity. My mother told me that at elections my grandfather would almost fawn on Lord Winterton when he called on him looking for his vote. One of my Conservative friends at Cambridge was Tam Dalyell, who later changed sides and became a Labour MP and eventually 'Father of the House' and plagued Margaret Thatcher over the sinking of the Argentine warship, *Belgrano*. Tam was a man of towering integrity, and I was sad to see that so little was done by his party to mark his passing. Perhaps he was just too good for them. Over three years I saw and heard the very many prominent people who visited the Union, and this was a great educator. I well remember Lady Astor's visit. She arrived in a magnificent black and yellow Rolls-Royce *coupe de ville*. She was riveting and I still like to repeat one of her jokes.

The Union Society was also a club, with an excellent and inexpensive restaurant and bar, comfortable lounges with newspapers and journals and a good library. When my parents visited me for a weekend in term time I liked to enjoy lunch with them in the Union Society restaurant. I remember on one occasion my father and I both wore our Sussex County Cricket Club members' ties, a distinctly non-collegiate symbol of solidarity. The bar was the occasional haunt of college fellows and alumni, one of whom was the suavely emollient Dr Glyn Daniel who for a long time hosted the popular 'museum' television programme 'Animal, Mineral, Vegetable?'. Another was the ancient rector of a village out in the fens, the Revd. Alan Goodman. (At the time he was probably much less ancient than I had presumed.) One of my undergraduate college friends was a professed agnostic and, motivated by missionary zeal, I arranged for him and the rector to come to tea with me in my lodgings with a view to weaning my friend away from his agnosticism. The debate was inconclusive and left my friend unmoved. In retrospect I am filled with admiration for the aged rector whose tolerance and Christian love made him give up an afternoon of what remained of his poor old life for the sake of a naïve and undersized undergraduate who had waylaid him in the bar of the Union when he was only trying to enjoy a quiet drink and possibly a nap. I hope that he is in Heaven. Looking back, I wonder whether I was also hoping that the light of revelation would fall on me as much as on my friend.

I spent my first two years in lodgings on the far side of the Mill Road railway bridge. It is unbelievable now, but within a stone's throw of my digs there was a cowshed with real cows where I would buy my half-pint of milk. As I was rather out of town I always made the most of my time in the city centre, often at the University Library which was for the whole three years a source of pure delight to me. I even arranged for someone to take me up and out on to the top of its tower to enjoy the view, and on another occasion the then Librarian, Mr. H.R. Creswick, kindly gave me a private view of a special exhibition. Second to the Library came the Fitzwilliam Museum, where I passed many hours in its galleries. This is where my interest in art and antiquities was nurtured, so that today they are a major preoccupation. I was never first-class degree material, and finished up with a two-two, which is unremarkably average. Had I concentrated on my studies rather more I might have notched it up to one better. But, *je ne regrette rien!*

Back home

After three years spent between Cambridge and home at Horsham, I more or less picked up where I had left off, living with my parents and now doing a job. I first travelled to London as an assistant editor with one of the world's foremost book publishers, Cassell, who at the time were publishing Winston Churchill, and on one occasion I found myself in the presence of the great man himself. I landed the job by writing around to the London publishers and struck lucky with Cassell and Company, one of the first six that I approached. They had been bombed out of their historic *Belle Sauvage* building on Ludgate Hill and had moved to old, ramshackle offices on St. Andrew's Hill, with the west front of St. Paul's Cathedral dominating the skyline over the rooftops. Some of the men shared a single lavatory cubicle where the antique pedestal was fashioned in the form of a Greek column (circa 1890?). The status of the loo's last occupant could always be judged from the aroma of the cigar that he left behind, 'trailing clouds of glory'?

I joined a team of five other editors and a secretary, an extremely pretty girl about my own age from the rather posh Mrs Hoster's academy. As the newcomer my desk was in the darkest recess of the back office, with the only view from the window a sloping slate roof of a warehouse, the kind of outlook favoured by filmset designers to portray a squalid part of New York, always including a red neon sign flashing intermittently, with one letter never lighting up, of course. The brain power on that third floor was formidable. *The Times* crossword resisted our combined assault for a matter of minutes only. Upstairs was the Art Department with artist Pauline Baynes, who was yet to find fame and presumably fortune as a renowned artist and lauded illustrator of Tolkien and C.S. Lewis.

The job was exactly what I had hoped for, editing the words of 'my' authors, reading the proofs and eventually handling the hardback copy, dust wrapper and all. Among 'my' authors were Nicholas Monsarrat, Alec Waugh and Frank Richards (the *Billy Bunter* books), and Soren Kierke-gaard, Stefan Zweig and Sheila Kaye-Smith (as reissues), *The*

Good Food Guide and many more. Alec Waugh was the elder brother of Evelyn, and I edited his novel, *Island in the Sun*. Maybe the film became better known than the book, but with a cast including James Mason, Joan Fontaine and Joan Collins, with a catchy theme tune sung by Harry Belafonte it's not surprising. The book's title was a much better than the one first chosen for it, which was *The Sugar Barons*.

My boss the Chief Editor, a kindly and mild-mannered professional, John Sundell, would hand over the typescript of a book that had been accepted for publication, and give me some guidance on what I should be looking out for when I read it. (With Monsarrat it was a matter of being aware of possible obscenity.) We had a collection of dictionaries and reference books, and our own copies of *Hart's Rules for Compositors and Readers*, and *The Authors' and Printers' Dictionary*, both from the O.U.P. Remember that computers were still decades away in the future. So I would check spelling and grammar and correct them and regularize any inconsistencies. Plots were also checked for inconsistencies, because mistakes here could be fatal for a detective novel, for example. More important was to look out for possible infringements of libel or copyright laws that could result in both author and publisher being fined at some point in the future. At the time, of course, it was also important to avoid breaking the laws regarding obscenity. The owner of Cassell was the highly successful publishing entrepreneur Sir Newman Flower, whose autobiography *Just As It Happened* is essential reading for the bookish. Flower came from Dorset, knew Thomas Hardy and became an authority on Handel, but must have had strict views on what was proper and what was not. It was said that he would never allow the word 'bugger' to appear in any book published by Cassell. I saw Sir Newman once or twice at St. Andrew's Hill, but, *de haut en bas*, we never spoke.

After signing off the typescript I would next see the book as galley proofs, the typeset pages printed in vertical strips of three pages. These I would read and correct and send copies to the author to do the same. The corrected galleys went back to the printer until finally 'page proofs' arrived made up in book form just in a brown paper cover. These were again read and returned, and at last we received a copy of the bound book complete with colourful dust wrapper or jacket. This copy would go straight into our collection as the 'file copy', so, should any errors come to light after publication, these would be noted in the book and corrected in the event of a re-print.

I joined the Society of Young Publishers and occasionally stayed on for an evening meeting. The only one that I remember was Malcolm Muggeridge speaking when he was editor of *Punch*. He bewailed the fact that satire was becoming more difficult because reality itself was becoming progressively more ridiculous, with the unthinkable becoming a kind of surreal norm. Oh, Muggeridge, thou shouldst be living at this hour! (As the saying goes, 'If he were alive today he'd be turning in his grave'.).

I managed to keep out of trouble, but did have an anxious moment when editing the UK edition of the memoirs of Grantland Rice, an American sports commentator who had written some harsh words about the French light-heavy-weight boxer Georges Carpentier, an opponent of Jack Dempsey. I assumed that Carpentier was dead, and the dead can't sue. But Georges landed a serious blow on me that evening when he appeared on my own television screen obviously in rude health. When I told John Sundell the next morning he calmed my fear by pointing out that the American edition had already gone through without any problem. (I noted later that when all this happened 'Granny' Rice himself was already dead!)

During my lunch breaks I delighted in being in the City of London and walking through its centuries of history from the days of Londinium to the present. Threading through those ancient lanes around St. Paul's I remember with great pleasure the sweet smell of warm beer coming through wide-open doorways as the pubs prepared for a new day, while out on the hot pavements it was the fruity whiff of London's drains. Some years later I felt truly at home when I was signed up as a Freeman of that unique city. Also later, as a governor of Collyer's School, which was under the tutelage of the Mercers' Company, I gained valuable insights into the charitable work of London's historic livery companies.

Yet the daily train and either bus or underground journey to London EC4 eventually wore me down, especially in the hot weather. So I left Cassells and for a short time I worked for a great 'character' at his newly-opened antiquarian bookshop in Arundel. The grey-bearded Alexander George Jameson-Benbrook was a gentleman antiquarian bookseller, a *persona* that he carefully cultivated right down to his monocle on a black ribbon and the immaculate vintage Rolls-Royce. (Its RR insignia was still painted red, denoting that it well pre-dated the death of Henry Royce in 1933.) He really was an officer (retired Lieutenant Commander) and a gentleman, and I was sorry to hear it when he died before his time. The journey to Arundel meant taking the train south instead of north, against the flow of nearly everyone else. It was Heaven, and the walk from the train station to the shop, along the water meadows with the grazing cattle just over the hedge, contrasted tellingly with the hell's kitchen of Victoria Station. But it was not to last. My employer, who appreciated, as we say, 'the best of everything,' found that the winter trade in Arundel could no longer allow him the luxury of an assistant and pay him £400 a year, so just before Christmas my parents came down in the old Vauxhall Velox, tied my pseudo-antique table to its roof, and brought me and my table back home. As a parting gift he gave me the one-volume *Dictionary of National Biography*, with his inscription: 'To John Snelling, who helped me build a ship'. Although I later collected more of the D.N.B. volumes, his is the one that I shall always keep.

I then changed course completely and joined the staff of the Swiss pharmaceutical company, CIBA, mainly because they were based in Horsham so that I could cycle to work. I went for one job and ended up with a different one that had not been advertised. I knew nothing about industry, so came without experience, which meant that I was teachable. I liked CIBA and CIBA liked me. The management were enlightened and humane, with the well-earned local reputation of being an enviable employer. Four years on, owing to the untimely death of my boss, I found myself promoted to be a full manager with a department of around 120 people, which at that time was a fair chunk of the workforce at the Horsham plant. I guess that in those days at 29 I was the youngest head of a department that they had ever had. The Horsham offices had inherited the traditional hierarchies of its Swiss parent, so I became the beneficiary of a semi-private washroom with a personal fresh linen hand towel replaced every morning. I worked and revelled in the beauty of that splendid art-deco building and the hands that framed its fearful symmetry.

In a matter of five years I had made the move from a City office editing Kierkegaard or *Billy Bunter* to running a large department in a hi-tech science-based industry. From the world of the Arts straight into the world of Science. I now ask myself, 'How on earth did that happen?' The answer is, 'I just don't know.' I am baffled by it. I have failed the ancient exhortation, γνῶθι σεαυτόν. It is really the story of all my life. I have 'received good measure, pressed down, shaken together and running over'. Perhaps it's just luck.

CIBA was a fast-growing business and I did not stay in charge of a huge department for very long, because growth required continuing re-organization. Then in the seventies came a merger with one of the other great Swiss companies, Geigy Pharmaceuticals, which entailed yet more changes. Latterly I worked entirely outside line-management on projects solely for the Director of Technical Operations. Over time I worked for two Technical Directors, now I'm afraid both dead. Their personalities were entirely different, but they both possessed a range of qualities that were wholly admirable. I could never have done their jobs, chiefly because I was not qualified and, I suppose, I was always rather attracted by the role of *eminence grise*, which was, no doubt, staying with the French, another *folie de grandeur* in itself.

CIBA and then CIBA-Geigy were highly respected companies, and now as components of the huge concern Novartis, still make a vibrant contribution, though unfortunately no longer in Horsham. In the early days I had the honour of serving one of CIBA's truly great managing directors as a personal assistant, Philip Mair, who was closely related to Lord Beveridge whose own place in our country's history is assured as the architect of Britain's post-war health service. I have to admit that accompanying Mair to London meetings in the chauffeur-driven Daimler, a model much favoured by royalty, certainly appealed to me. ('*Vanity, vanity*, saith the Preacher.') A later charismatic managing Director of CIBA-Geigy was John Perkins, who, straight after Cambridge as a young man, had commanded a motor torpedo boat in the North Sea. He inflicted serious losses on the enemy, many times escaped death by inches and ended the war with two Distinguished Service Crosses. Then, having been called to the bar, he entered Industry. I shall always picture him at a staff party with a bottle in each hand and a girl on each arm. Everyone, especially the men and women 'on the shop floor', loved him, and quite rightly so. I think that we all did. He was a gold brick cast in the mould of Churchill.

I had no wish to move out of the family home and neither did my parents wish me to. My parents were loving and wise and well balanced and wonderful to be with and we complemented and enhanced one another's lives until they both died. There was always a light-heartedness and much laughter. To paraphrase Samuel Johnson, 'We were a nest of singing birds'. My mother possessed great personal warmth and was entirely selfless, without a single selfish gene in her body. Of all the people I have known, she must be the front-runner in the Eternal Life Stakes. We all loved life. And all this was against the background of an extended loving family of aunts, uncles and cousins spread over three generations. That I might be married myself never even crossed my mind. This may be because I was born with a form of dwarfism that meant that I never grew taller than five feet, so from the start I rather ruled myself out as marriageable. In those days and in my world, sleeping with someone was a big deal, and was not something done on the second occasion after first shaking hands with them. A lady did once suggest that she and I should marry. The idea was couched in jocular words but meant seriously. I'm afraid that I continued to treat it as a joke, but though I may have been meant for her, I never felt that she was meant for me, and that's all that I am prepared to write about that. However, I subsequently enjoyed many happy years in a close relationship with a woman with a Master of Science degree and much younger than I was. She utterly changed my life. And that's all that I am prepared to say about that, too.

But back to church affairs. Having become familiar with the format of the Sung Eucharist at Cambridge and appreciating it, I found that this had been happening at Holy Trinity for a long time. So quite soon my mother and I and frequently Brian Masters attended regularly. And then H.T. had a change of priest-in-charge and before he arrived we were told that he was Irish. We were not particularly admiring of the then Vicar of Horsham, the Revd. R.C.O. Goodchild, whom we considered to be a bit of a smooth *apparatchik* and we thought that the new curate would be putty in his manipulating hands. (Goodchild later became Bishop of Kensington and died in 1998.) So before he arrived I had dubbed the new man 'Father O' Tool'. I was wrong. Michael Cochrane, high church Anglican from Belfast, turned out to be nobody's tool. His ministry in Horsham lasted twenty years and his close friendship with me and my family and friends went on for many more years until his death in 2000. For ten years we went on foreign holidays together and Michael was an ideal courier since he had already visited many places with church parties, and had a working knowledge of German. Abroad we attended Catholic masses (without receiving the communion) and I remember that in Rome for the first time naturally we went to the Vatican and St. Peter's. Michael knelt to pray at that great marble 'rail' of the high altar above the tomb of Saint Peter. I did not join him there and I have since wondered what it was that stopped me. The rest of this essay could easily be all about Michael Cochrane, but more about him follows this memoir. Educated at the Queen's University, Belfast, he was well-read, empathetic, humane, entertaining company and steadfast in the faith of the Church. In twenty years in the parish he christened babies who later came back to his church to be married by him. In the earlier years especially he contributed to furthering my own education.

In due course I became Warden at Holy Trinity and served on parish committees and eventually decided to study to become lay reader. This would involve wearing a cassock and among other things learning how to deliver sermons from the pulpit. Michael and I went to a tailor and church robe maker just off The Strand in London to be measured for my cassock, and one day during one of our visits someone came in with some ecclesiastical garments for dry cleaning. These apparently belonged to the then Archbishop of Canterbury, who evidently tended to drop food down his front in industrial quantities, something that I now do myself with predictable regularity. I did wear my cassock a few times and gave my M.A. hood an airing when I sang evensong. I was once asked to preach at the main service on a Remembrance Sunday. I believe that I was given the job because the curate of the time didn't really know what to say, and now I cannot remember what I said, but whatever it was I probably would not be saying it today. I had only just started some rather desultory study for the reader's course when I discovered that I had cataracts, one eye worse than the other. This was the beginning of over forty years of eye surgery and medical attention that goes on still. But the first cataract gave me a reason for giving up the idea of becoming a lay reader, because, in spite of applying to become one, try as I may I just could not see myself clambering up into a pulpit to declaim as fact many things that I myself still did not fully understand and did not really believe all of those that I did. For a good many years I had been attracted by those theologians who embraced the science of evolution and its consequences, like Charles Raven, Pierre Teilhard de Chardin the Jesuit priest and scholar, whose *Phenomenon of Man* and *Le Milieu Divin* (in English) sat on my shelves along with the current issues of the journal *Theology*. (The Internet tells me that he calls Teilhard a charlatan. This implies an intention to deceive, which I believe is as untrue as it is uncharitable.) Also on my shelves there were Sir Alister Hardy's *The Biology of God* as well as the more orthodox offerings by J.A. Baker (*The Foolishness of God*), Robinson's (*Honest to God*), Karen Armstrong, Hans Kung and others. The Revd. Harry Williams CR is also in there. Sadly, most of these eagerly bought books were never read right through, as they were competing with the need to follow a career and enjoy a social life, albeit a social life that included 'church' as well as, at different times, the Round Table movement and, then, for 42 years, Rotary International. The Rotary and Inner Wheel Clubs in Horsham played a large part in the lives of both my parents and me. The movement is a wonderful way to make lasting friendships and to turn good intentions into realities for the benefit of everyone, near and far.

Time passed and we all grew older. My father died in 1975 after long treatment for raised blood pressure, from which his mother had also suffered. If there is any justice he must be in Heaven with that old Cambridgeshire rector. I had already bought a roomy bungalow on a third of an acre of gardens with the idea of my parents and I all moving there together, so when it came to it there were only the two of us to move. My mother was intellectually as sharp as ever, though increasingly troubled by arthritis she continued to cook and run the house, with domestic help and a gardener, both coming for just one afternoon a week. She was eighty in 1984 and I discovered that the rules of my pension scheme would allow me to retire in 1985, though on a greatly curtailed pension, of course. I reasoned that if my mother and I were to enjoy the remains of her life together, then I would have to retire to give us the time to do it. So in 1985 I retired as a senior manager of the Technical Operations Division of CIBA-Geigy, and I was pleased that later I was commissioned to write the company's history which it privately published as *Makers of Medicine* in 1989.

We continued with life as usual, with the addition of motoring trips to other parts of the country on 'mini-breaks'. I never once regretted the bargain I had made to exchange income for the precious commodity of time. In due course my mother, and to some extent I myself, began succumbing to arthritis, and my mother became subject to angina pain. She, and eventually I too, began to use wheelchairs. (My *spinal stenosis* came to me a good deal later on.) I had always dreaded the inevitable time when my mother would die. I recall raising this question with her when I was about thirteen, one afternoon during the war when we were walking home from the town. Her reply was, 'You must have faith, duck.' Duck did not interrogate her any further. In 2001 after only 36 hours in the local hospital my mother died, shortly before her 97TH birthday. From the day she went to hospital I began to sleep where a phone was – in her bedroom. After years of dreading this cataclysmic event for so long I was surprised at how well I reacted to everything. It is a cliché that God gives us an unexpected strength to ride out the storm, and at the time this was my explanation. This did not stop me from shedding many tears when alone, which is something I have always been prone to do, and I still am.

A sadness in the family was the illness and death from multiple sclerosis of my cousin Sally. (Fortunately, research into the illness has considerably improved a patient's prospects since then.) Sally was the daughter of my mother's only, and younger, sister Win. I was twelve when she was born and was as near as I came to having a sister. Over the years she would accompany my mother and me, separately or together, on all kinds of events and outings. At the end she could only lie motionless flat on her bed in a nursing home, a pad placed into each of her poor little hands to prevent her fingers involuntarily clenching and cutting into her palms. That scene will always stay with me and move me to tears. I had witnessed her life and been part of it from birth to death, so can feel for parents who continue to live on after their child has died. To witness a complete life from beginning to end, a kind of life capsule, nothing here before it and nothing here after it, one then cannot help wondering what the purpose of it was; if it comes to that what the purpose of any life is. It is the oldest of old questions which the Church attempted to answer in The Catechism. The fact that today even the most active churchgoers have never even heard of The Catechism shows how successful the Anglican church has been in quietly dumping it. Any attempt to explain the unexplainable or to know the unknowable is bound to fail. We repeatedly declare that God is unknowable but, that has never stopped all and sundry telling us exactly what He wants. For an example, half the Anglican Church thinks that He wants same-sex marriage while the other half declares that to be a mortal sin and one of the last things that He would want. So, assuming that God actually has an opinion on the matter, we are no nearer to knowing what it is.

Sunt lachrimae rerum et mentem mortalia tangunt

Sometimes the only answer to the apparent purposelessness suffering of mankind is tears of pity. At the time of writing these words thousands of men, women and children are dying while trying to escape the life they have. Picture a little boy or girl, say about four, wrapped up against the cold as well as a loving parent could manage being lifted from a sinking vessel and, seeing a camera, reacts with a little smile. The child has no idea why it's there but manages a childish smile. Surely that child is a microcosm of everybody who suffers, from all those ills the flesh is heir to, from sickness, bereavement, poverty, from cruelty. And just like the child in the boat those people have no idea why they are there to suffer those things, but, like the child, they manage a smile. Surely, that's worth a few tears, not only of pity but also of sheer admiration for humankind. With empathy for our fellow human beings hate becomes impossible and only pity and love remain. From what we know, when freed from all the accretions of ancient doctrine and dogma, Jesus the man remains the template and the example. *Ecce homo* indeed!

Revelstoke

Somewhere not far from Revelstoke in the Canadian Rockies there is The Great Divide, a watershed that divides the east from the west. On one side of it the continental waters flow towards the Atlantic and on the other they reach the Pacific. In my memoir we have here found ourselves at the Revelstoke point. So far my life story has taken us from year zero on a tranquil journey of faith, but now the waters on their journey to the sea are rippled by questioning and some scepticism. Even so, I must record that for me personally my journey through the *valle lacrimum*, as the Vulgate describes life, has mainly been one of warmth and sunlight and I have never once regretted setting out on it, even though I, nor anyone else, had a choice in the matter.

In embarking on this memoir it had been my intention to conclude it with a final section entitled 'Post Revelstoke'. In this section I had intended to highlight those traditional beliefs that my experience of living has simply worn away and for me made them no longer tenable. I have found that within the catalogue of beliefs that I inherited as a cradle

Anglican some contradict each other. So this has led me to stray from the path of traditional doctrine and to explore new ways of regarding Jesus and his significance for us today. But what would be the point in setting down those words here? Whether it was Solomon or Hezekiah who was responsible for the Old Testament book *Ecclesiastes*, he spoke truly – 'There is nothing new under the sun', and better scholars than I am will have already raised some of the issues for me, and more eloquently. Folk reading these words so far will have the will and the wit and be capable of discovering their words for themselves. For me, it all remains a work in progress. We know just enough to know that we don't know much. By all means we can allow the discoveries of Science to shape our approach to Theology, but we also know how one minute the latest scientific answer is lauded only to be later derided and then trampled under foot. So whether we buy into orthodox belief or orthodox atheism, *caveat emptor*!

In spite of all the curses that the Internet has laid upon us, it has also brought us the world and the sum of its knowledge. Just like life itself, Faith must develop and cannot just stop, say, in the year 1300, which was the year in which that faithful monk produced the Mappa Mundi of Hereford Cathedral, showing his world and not *our* world. (In *his* world its western edge of it was the Straits of Gibraltar.) All religions, including our own, suffer from a short-sighted localism that renders them either indifferent or hostile to parallel cultures and beliefs. Surely, those believing that there is a 'God the Creator', who created everything, then they must also believe that that same god also created and loves those with parallel cultures and beliefs? So the question for all those of Paul's 'household of faith' is, 'do you believe that God created everything, or was it we who created *God* in order to explain the world?' 'No,' we chorus, 'God created everything!'

And yet how few of us act as though this is true.

Yet the Anglican Church will always be 'my tribe', it's music, liturgy and it's hymnology are so part of me that my blood group should be registered as 'O-Positive C of E'. I love it and it's people. They are *my* people. In any case, loving all people really is not that difficult. After all, are we not all, from the most exalted to the most wretched, fellow passengers on that same ship on that same journey, on that same ultimate voyage of discovery?

Ο γέγραφα γέγραφα

Apologia Plus

1. Bishop Brian Masters

After writing an obituary of 'Bishop Brian' for Collyer's School I then offered it to the London diocesan archive which graciously accepted it. So here is a different version for my own archive, as an appendix to Apologia.

After serving as deacon and priest at St. Dunstan's Stepney, a big East End parish with a handful of priests living together in a clergy house, Brian was appointed to be vicar of Holy Trinity in the Hoxton area of London, and this is where his mother, by then a widow, joined him as his house-keeper after uprooting herself from the family home in Sussex. So this unsophisticated countrywoman with limited experience, neither urban nor urbane, found herself trans-planted into a forest of high-rise flats and the heartland of Cockney culture. The Victorian vicarage bordered on the hideous, inside the brick walls institutionally painted over in dark green, with the living rooms in the basement which entailed a journey upstairs every time someone came to the door, which was often. Beggars were frequently at that door, and Grace came to know some of them by name. The church itself was old-fashioned high Anglican, what used to be known as Anglo-Catholic, giving people the feeling that they had unwittingly strayed into a back street church in Naples. Something that cannot be measured was the warmth of the welcome that the parishioners gave to Grace Masters and her lanky son. Thanks to the warm-heartedness of the Hoxton congregation town and country instantly bonded. In the age of the notorious Krays this was difficult territory for an incumbent, with fights by criminal gangs sometimes spilling into the streets. What could a priest, attired in biretta and cape going home late at night, do but pass by on the other side? Once, when my mother visited Mrs Masters in Hoxton and Brian was walking with them in the street thus attired, they passed a group of small children, when one small boy confided to another, 'That's Jesus, that is.'

In due course 'Jesus' was made the Bishop of Fulham, then a non-territorial appointment to look after the un-beneficed clergy. This meant moving from Hoxton, so mother and son next found themselves in an apartment in a kind of Mayfair Millionaires' Row in North Audley Street, where the corner shop was Selfridges. The contrast to the earlier tied house was extreme. Yet Grace continued to take in her stride the ever-burning security lights of her Arab neighbours and the street clutter of Rolls-Royces.

The last appointment was to become the Bishop of Edmonton, the title taken from an area of North London and consisting of over a hundred parishes in a wedge-shaped segment with some in the centre of London and even more towards the periphery. This entailed another move, this time to another tall house grafted on to the end of a typical Regent's Park terrace. Although Brian's study cum office was on the semi-ground floor, everything else was upstairs, so Grace still had these to contend with. At home my mother and Grace had been members of the Women's Institute, and all through these years Grace had been a frequent weekend guest with us at Horsham. So my mother and I at one time or another had visited all the London homes of our friends 'the Masters'.

It was at Regent's Park that I met an assortment of clergy, including a Bishop of London (and his cat-loving wife), and an assortment of other bishops and clergy. One of the bishops I met there (the late Rt. Revd. John Hughes) I rather admired because he not only traditionally wore the episcopal amethyst but had reverted to the Tudor practice of placing his signet ring on his forefinger, giving him a hand that Holbein might have painted. It was during a tour of the house shortly after the Masters moved in that I noticed the only photograph standing by the bishop's bedside was of Pope John Paul the Second. It was more than likely inscribed by His Holiness.

During the mid 1990s Brian was getting geared up to celebrate his mother's 90TH birthday ('I don't want a fuss, Brian') when she died. Her body was returned to Horsham to be buried with her husband, Stanley, at Hills Cemetery. Brian must have missed her enormously and found life without her very strange indeed.

Brian died on 23RD September 1998. He had a heart attack in his study quite early in the morning and was taken to hospital, but there was nothing that could be done.

I believe that during his episcopate Brian received a certain amount of media attention because gay activists claimed that he was gay but concealed the fact and been hypocritical about it. The issue deserves airing here, as I am confident that no one has known him better for longer than I have, although in his later years we did meet much less frequently. I have to say that from when Brian was about twelve when I first knew him until he died, nothing at all in his speech or behaviour ever gave me the slightest impression that he could be homosexual. I have always thought of him as being highly cerebral and quite a-sexual, with no noticeable libido of any kind, in one direction or another. I always doubted that he was capable of generating enough emotional heat to embark on anything as intense as a sexual relationship. That is not to say that his job did not bring him into contact with gay clergy or that he didn't accept that as simply a fact of life and the need to go with the flow. Yet against his apparent emotional coolness one must set the real affection which many members of the immigrant population felt for him. There is a photograph of the bishop surrounded by a group of laughing West Indian children while one of them is trying on his mitre. One could have warmed one's hands on that photograph, such was the love and affection it revealed. So where was this rather austere prelate that I have depicted for you? After all those years, am I the one who has entirely misread him?

I hired a car and driver to take me to Brian's funeral at St. Paul's Cathedral where I joined members of the family at the Deanery before going across to the cathedral. Being in a wheelchair I was taken up from ground level by a lift in the south transept. I had a place with the family in a semicircular arc of chairs beneath the great dome. At first I felt that I was entering a film-set, so bright was the lighting. The coffin was covered in a gold vestment with a gold mitre on it in front of the nave altar. There were probably twenty or so bishops, and in the transepts a couple of hundred clergy. The nave was full of everyone else, and when the singing began the wall of sound sweeping up from the vast congregation delivered an emotional shock that was almost physical. The service was the whole of the beautiful Fauré Requiem. The Bishop of London celebrated the Communion and gave the funeral oration, and the Bishop of York recited the Commendation.

The hearse and cars were drawn up at the bottom of the steps at the west front, while many of the congregation crowded the steps to see the courtege leave. The bells of St. Paul's were ringing a muffled peal. I was given a place in the first car behind the hearse with clergy who were closest to Brian, while my own car followed on with other mourners. Some of the crowd wept, made the sign of the cross, clapped and waved as we drew away from the steps and pulled out into Ludgate Hill. The undertaker walked ahead of the hearse for a bit, but as we were on our way to Brookwood Cemetery nearly forty miles away he soon hopped into the hearse and away we went, right through London from east to west and into Surrey. The mitre, which had again been placed on top of the coffin, quite soon slipped off it. Throughout the journey I found the conversation in that first funeral car fascinating, but it goes no further than the next full stop.

As the old London burial grounds had become full, some of the London churches acquired overflow plots in the 'new' vast cemetery at Brookwood. One of these was St. Alban's Church in Holborn, which was a prominent church in the Edmonton episcopal area, and this was where it's bishop's body was buried with due ceremony.

The little boy in the grey flannel short-trousers suit, whom I first met in 1943 when he joined class 1A at Collyer's School, had travelled a very long way to rest in a bishop's grave in Surrey.

2. The Revd. Michael Cochrane

This was my contribution to the local paper after the death of Michael Cochrane

The sudden death occurred last week of the Revd. Michael Cochrane, who was Priest-in-Charge of Holy Trinity Church, Horsham, from 1956 to 1976, before becoming Vicar of Aldwick.

Michael Cochrane was born in Belfast, and after a distinguished academic career at Queen's University there, he read for the Ministry at Lincoln Theological College. Before coming to Horsham he was Curate of St. George's, Headstone, near Harrow, where he was working at the time of the train disaster there, and it made a lasting impression on him.

As an approachable and caring pastor, Michael Cochrane made many friends, both inside and outside the Church, and his mother, Eunice, who kept house for him until her death in 1974, also had a particular empathy for ordinary people of the Common area who found themselves in trouble.

Both Michael Cochrane and his mother loved Horsham and its people, a fact denoted by his unusually long ministry for a second curacy of nearly twenty years. At Holy Trinity he built up the church youth club and young wives group, took many holiday parties abroad, and saw through the successful building of a new Trinity Hall adjoining the church. He was a supporter of the Horsham Music Circle, and sometimes acted as props and costume manager for a local drama group. His concern for others and his lively conversational gifts ensured that Michael Cochrane was a welcome asset in so many areas of Horsham life. Yet at the centre was his strong faith, love of the Anglican Church, and a determination to carry out its worship and liturgy to the highest possible standards.

After Aldwick Michael Cochrane retired to Surrey, and continued to preach and take services in neighbouring churches of Bisley, Lightwater and Pirbright. A requiem will be held at Holy Trinity on Saturday at 1pm, and the funeral at Bisley on Thursday next.

Copy of my letter to Michael Cochrane's brother Patrick who lived with his wife in Belfast. At this time Patrick was receiving treatment for cancer from which he died shortly afterwards.

26TH February 2000

Dear Patrick, (*handwritten*)

Thank you very much for the copy of your letter to the clergy – it is fine. I had told Graham Low (*the current* team *vicar of Holy Trinity*) that you were writing. He said he would gladly add your name to the Holy Trinity prayer list for a good outcome from your operation.

I said I would give details of Michael's service, and I am only sorry it has taken me so long to do it. We have been a bit distracted because Cis has been poorly, and we have an appointment for her to see a consultant on 10TH March. We hope it is nothing serious, but it obviously must be attended to.

St. John the Baptist Church Bisley lies down a tree-lined path, which runs off a lane off the main road. It has a little churchyard, and an enormous yew tree outside the main door. It effectively make a natural roundabout for turning round to come out. Like a lot of Surrey churches, there is a small gabled porch at the west end. The church itself is quite small, a central aisle and additional aisle added on the north side. The chancel is quite small, with timbered roof beams. The altar has an embroidered frontal, and two wrought iron candlesticks and cross. All the inside of the church is painted white. There are oak pews. There are no steps anywhere, except a shallow one between the nave and chancel.

The church was full, with a number I knew from Horsham, (Carole Moule had driven up from Gloucestershire), and many others, of course from the Bisley area and Aldwick whom I did not know. Sally's brother, Michael, and his wife, came down from Harrow. (Michael is a house-master at Harrow School.)

The coffin was covered with a gold chasuble, and on top a cross of white flowers, with smaller flowers gathered at the centre. The clergy and readers, about a dozen, sat either side of it in the chancel. The Rector spoke about Michael very well, and a copy of his words is due to be circulated by Alan. The Revd. Nicholas Flint was sitting in the congrega-tion, and went up to the lectern to read the lesson, and the Revd. David Jones from Wales said the prayers. I think you have seen the service leaflet, so there is not much more to add, except that as the procession left the church the organist played Nimrod from the Enigma Variations. The service was moving and dignified, but not without its lighter moments when reference was made to Michael's own humour and engaging mannerisms. At the end, many of the congregation were visibly moved by the ceremony.

Your cousin G**** sat behind me, and I made myself known to him. Although Michael had spoken about him, I did not realize how very deformed the poor chap is – but he is very sharp, and does not let it get him down. The Revd. Anthony Freeman, who was a server at Holy Trinity, and is now a writer and theologian, much influenced by Michael, was intending to attend, but he unexpectedly had to take a service down in Exeter where he lives. Carol Jessop, former organist at HT, was also coming, but was very poorly and unable to come from Oxfordshire. They both phoned me.

(Numerous people in Horsham had phoned me after the news of Michael's passing, to express their shock and sense of loss.)

My friend, who drove me, and I did not go on to the crematorium, so I cannot say anything about that side of it.

I now have the copies of the tapes of the requiem at Holy Trinity, and am pleased to enclose one. My reading the lesson did not record well, as I had no personal microphone. I am also pleased to enclose the relevant pages of the local paper of 4TH February. I took the *Church Times* of last Friday, but can see nothing in there. I will check to see if it is in this week's.

Hope you and Betty are bearing up, in the difficult circumstances. Will be in touch again soon.

Usual sign-off

John
Ps. I hear that the *Church Times* of this week has a letter from Nicholas, so I will try to get a copy for you.

More of the Revd. Michael Cochrane

Born 29TH November 1924. Died 26TH January 2000

Michael Cochrane arrived in Horsham in 1956 to become Priest-in-Charge at Holy Trinity after a first curacy at St. George's, Headstone, near Harrow. He was 32. No one knew then that he would remain in Horsham for nearly twenty years as a pillar of the Parish, and, on a personal note, I had no idea that he would grow into one of my closest friends and virtually a member of my family until the day of his death.

A page or so of type cannot begin to describe the many facets of this most unusual man. Those meeting him for the first time would probably be struck by the unstoppable, mercurial talk, always witty and robust, and apparently at once at odds with his perceived profession. If most people carry a mental stereotype of the Anglican clergyman in their heads, then Michael Cochrane was emphatically not it. If, on the other hand, one thinks of a good man, literate, widely read and above all humane, then that would be nearer the mark. And he was entirely without social or secular prejudice.

Norman Michael John Antony Ferguson Cochrane was born in County Down near Belfast and did well at the Queen's University there, and partly no doubt due to his soft, 'educated Ulster' accents, most people put his trenchancy and ebullience down to his 'Irishness'. However it came about, few people left his presence without a smile and an intangible feeling that the world wasn't such a bad place after all. In short, an encounter with Michael unfailingly supported and lifted the spirits, and in so many desperately sad pastoral situations of tragedy and bereavement, that was a divine gift.

He accomplished it, of course, because in everything he did his own steadfast faith and belief in the goodness of God were at the centre of it, and it could not help but show through. His loving concern for others, whether or not they were 'church people', was manifested in a thousand different ways, whether just being there when needed, remembering birthdays, visiting, and, of course, praying, bringing all these concerns to God. Yet conventional expressions of piety never passed his lips.

Sometimes the inner and the outer aspects of his life appeared in stark contrast – as when an old lady parishioner became incapable of looking after herself. It was Michael who faced the stench and took a spade to the accretion of ordure over the bedroom floor, sustained first by celebrating an early Eucharist and then in situ by the strongest of Gauloises cigarettes.

Throughout his ministry Michael was ever the perfectionist, the liturgy always proper and well-ordered, church vestments laundered and in good array. Unpunctuality, slothfulness, in fact anything approaching the 'sloppy' were anathema to him. More than once while we were travelling in Italy we have passed priests or monks, their beards clogged with stale food and their robes shiny with grease, and he has exploded, 'Stinking with dirt! Why on earth can't they be holy and clean at the same time!'

Over a lifetime of priestly service, the statistics must be awe-inspiring – the number of early services, the number of marriages, the deathbeds, the visits, in his case the thousands of miles he walked on parish duties – mercifully, he never took the wheel of a car. Neither was navigating his strongest point – once, after a frustrating drive through Valetta, I discovered that he had been holding the map upside down.

Even so, Michael's gifts were formidable. We remember him writing brilliant songs for the parish harvest suppers, singing, playing the 'cello at a church concert, preparing the Trinity church suppers in the 'old' Trinity Hall, year after year organizing the town's Christian Aid collections, supporting local drama and music clubs, always enjoying the social pleasures of the Church and Town, but never, never compromising or forgetting his vocation.

At Holy Trinity he built up the Youth Club, set up the Young Wives' Group, planned and completed the Mariana Talbot memorial garden for the repose of ashes, and before leaving to become Vicar of Aldwick was instrumental in the building of the new Trinity Hall adjoining the church. It was typical of him that when the hall's foundation stone came to be laid, he invited every member of the congregation, one after the other, to give it a tap.

Sadly, there is no space here to mention the unique ministry of Michael's mother, Eunice, who lent a sympathetic ear to many in the Common area of Horsham until her untimely death in 1974. After retirement from Aldwick in 1990 Michael lived in Surrey, and was busy taking services in Bisley, Lightwater and Pirbright. He leaves a brother and sister-in-law in Belfast, cousins, numerous godchildren and very many friends. The lives of all will be immeasurably poorer without him.

4. Another Thought For The Day

I can't remember how long I have been listening to *Thought For The Day*, the mini-sermon that crops up before the eight o'clock news on Radio 4's *Today* programme. Like the Church itself, how it's changed over the years. Some time ago the same contributor did a week's stint at a time, but now, lest boredom should set in after three minutes, there's a different speaker every day. And in earlier years the talk always started and ended with a few bars of music. No more. Which is a pity, since the music often had more to say than the words. So often the contributors hurry through their scripts, which are unfailingly 'politically correct' and frequently laden with jargon. (If I hear the words 'outreach' or 'marginalised' once more, I shall immediately become a fully paid-up *Heretick.)

The most impressive *Thought* that I ever heard was delivered so slowly that one feared the man would actually be meeting his maker face to face before it finished. It was compulsive listening, rather like a death-bed confession must be. Yet after twenty years or so, it's some of the tunes used to round off the talk that still dwell in the mind – the opening of Elgar's first symphony, and a snatch of the Fauré Requiem *In Paradisum* being just two. (I've always felt some mysterious rapport with much of Elgar's music. He and I seem to be wired-up in the same invisiblele circuitry, and a few bars can go straight to the soul. Other music may do the same for you.)

I once thought that I would like to have a shot at doing

Thought For The Day myself, but wisdom prevailed. I feared that my personal larder of faith and doctrine might prove too meagrely stocked to feed the nation's higher needs. And how daunting to be scheduled to speak straight after some prominent death or disaster, with no time to rewrite the script. While the country waits to be uplifted or reassured, just saying 'It's all as big a mystery to me as it is to you, just have faith, etc.' is not what they want to hear, although dressed up more professionally that's probably what they would get from many another.

I used to think that words can express anything, but now I am far from certain. Frequently I find that the thought is just too fragile to be committed to words. There is just no way of articulating some things, and when we speak it doesn't all come out like plonking a pile of spaghetti on to a plate – one word must follow another, there's not even room for two abreast. So half-way through your sentence your listener has often raced ahead of you and usually ended up in the wrong place with completely the wrong end of the stick.

We may have talented teachers and preachers, but I'll wager that it's music that moves us more and stays longer in the memory than words do. Words are akin to an ointment, but music is an injection straight into the bloodstream. The music of great composers, well-loved hymns, the magnificent settings of our liturgy, they can all lift a corner of the curtain to reveal at least some of that other world of the spirit, the eternal that lies behind the transient.

The musical excellence of the Church of England, of all

churches for that matter, should be cherished and preserved. In the parish of Horsham we are fortunate indeed in having not only lively and talented musicians to carry on the formal worship, we also preserve the tradition of bringing the music of the world into our churches and halls for the benefit of everyone. Music can be a pilgrim's sturdy staff for us all. What about that as a thought for the day!

* *In this context the spelling of heretick is correct.*

5. 'Fred's Gone For The Spike'

How I know about 'the spike' I'll tell you later. It happened because I was born into a rather unusual family business, which started with my grandfather, John. He was the son of a poor country couple, and first saw the light of day in 1870, and at the age of ten he was standing in a Sussex field flapping his arms around as a kind of 'scarecrow vivant'. Even John's rustic parents agreed that a career in crow-scaring was a bit short of development potential, and when the time came for their son John to get a proper job, a local stonemason took him on as an apprentice.

This was a good move. John had talent and did well as a stonemason, and in 1895 he married his sweetheart, Fanny, a Horsham girl. and they settled down there. A nice little job turned up when a Brighton 'gels' school decided to move out of the town and to build a new place up on the cliffs, so John and Fanny moved to Brighton, where John joined an army of tradesmen in the creation of Roedean. You may have noticed, it's still there.

Like a couple of Thomas Hardy characters, John and Fanny then moved back to Horsham where his next task was to fashion the stonework for a new church to replace a corrugated-iron job, Holy Trinity. Like Roedean, this took the best part of two years, and by the end of it John felt he knew enough about the trade to strike out on his own, and anyway maybe both of them had grown tired of traipsing around. So John rented a house with a little yard close to 'his' church, and set himself up as a general mason, willing as well to make memorials for the local churchyards and cemeteries. This is where they had a daughter, and she turned out to be my mother.

In John's day the cutting and shaping of blocks of stone was a back-breaking business, with no machinery to help. Two men, one either end of a huge, shark-toothed saw, would alternately drag it to and fro across the stone block until it finally fell apart, and then they'd start over again. They achieved the finer shaping by repeated use of a broad-ended chisel, continually thumped by a wooden-headed mallet the size of a pumpkin. (When I was old enough to hold it, John gave his grandson a tiny mallet of his own.) John continually checked his men's work, and on one occasion chided a mason on the quality. 'Well, it's near enough,' grunted the mason. 'Near enough ain't good enough,' declaimed John. 'Go back and do it again.' When the mason called him over for a second look, John stared at it for a while, then grudgingly admitted, 'That's near enough'.

The geology of Britain offers a wonderful choice of

materials for the mason, from the granites of Cornwall and Scotland to the green slate of the Lake District, the so-called marble of Purbeck and the sandstones of the Midlands. But the most controversial of all the monumental mason's materials just has to be marble, and white marble at that. Quarried extensively from the days of Classical Greece and Rome, there it is, inside every place of worship from the tiniest country church to the grandest of our cathedrals, piled to the clerestories with marble. And yet today, outside in the open air, marble is far from welcome in many an English churchyard, as being discordant and alien.

Luckily for my grandfather, a hundred years ago the artistic sensitivities of archdeacons and vicars were less finely tuned. Italy rejoiced in possessing not only the marble but also the craftsmen to turn it into finished memorials, and soon English mourners were able to buy from their local stonemason a variety of statues and figures that they would have seen only in their dreams. Their quality was perfect, but they could also be excruciatingly sentimental – angels, complete with marble feathered wings sighing over the departed; disconsolate cherubs holding a single lily, in fact everything that today most people would hate as hideously mawkish and over-the-top. One day, when my grandfather and helpers were manoeuvring a near life-size angel into his small display window, they lost their grip and the heavenly being fairly flew – for the first and last time – clean through the glass window and into the street. Only the expression on the angel's face remained beatific.

When John started his business, he used a wagon pulled

by a single horse. The weak spot here tended to be the horse, since John could never resist a bargain, and usually ended up with a nag that had seen better days. Every Wednesday was the town market day, and unlike the Mayor of Casterbridge, he didn't sell things he didn't want, he bought them, and it was after a visit to the market that he proudly returned leading a fresh horse, which was fine until a marching band passed by and the new horse at once began dancing down the road on its hindlegs, which wasn't easy once it was between the shafts. Only then did John discover that the creature was fresh from a circus, and had found adapting to a less glamorous lifestyle just too much!

As a boy I watched my father inscribing names on the stones, tap, tap, tap with his special heavy hammer onto a sharp chisel. That hammer is still a treasured keepsake of mine. Only too often he had known the faces behind the names. No room for mistakes here, a wrong or misshaped letter could spoil an entire inscription and ruin a stone tablet. At best it might then be re-cycled as a headstone over some toff's favourite gundog, but more often, like a gangster's victim, it disappeared below ground somewhere as part of a foundation.

But, best of all, was going into country churchyards with my father while he set up memorials. So I stood by watching as he and helpers installed the memorials. In this way I saw much of Sussex and Surrey through all the changing seasons. This realm can boast of some wonderful little country churchyards, many of them better by far than the one at Stoke Poges, which inspired old Thomas Gray to pen his famous *Elegy*. But my reaction to them was always the same as his In Sussex we are blessed with so many beautiful churchyards but in springtime Wiggonholt near Pulborough and Oakwood Hill in Surrey take some beating.

Travelling around with my dad I also became acquainted with that dedicated breed of men and women, the church sexton. Maybe they weren't even called that – they were just 'the person who looks after the churchyard', but almost every churchyard had one. Often with little formal education, and living within a blackbird's call of the church, these heroes worked long hours in church and churchyard, mowing, repairing, cleaning, digging, planting, pruning, all for next to no reward except the love of their charges, and, ultimately, one supposes, of God. Sometimes the Vicar recognized them for the stalwarts that they were, and sometimes those same stalwarts were completely invisible to the 'men of the cloth'. In those days, it was only men of the cloth.

Now I said I'd tell you about the spike. It was simply a kind of doorbell for the departed, a long steel rod rammed down into a grave to find out if there was anyone at home. Sometimes the sexton needed to know how deep a coffin was buried, so he found out. When he hit something solid, he'd reached 'the box' or its contents. You never know, there could always be 'room for one more on top'. This may have been a rather macabre idea for a little boy to grasp, but I suppose it just comes of being born into a rather unusual business.

All this was a long time ago, and, with no third generation willing to follow in my grandfather's footsteps, (both I and my younger cousin went to Cambridge on state scholarships, and have enjoyed different careers), the business that he started over a century ago was in the end more or less just given to a local firm of undertakers providing they kept the name alive. But I'll wager there's one thing that doesn't change. I guess that there will still be a stalwart dedicated to cherishing a churchyard not far from you, and that somewhere in his shed he'll have a spike. I also wager that, regardless of job title, he or she is still living within a blackbird's call of that blessed plot, and is healthy, and contented, and probably sleeps more soundly at night than you, or I, or most of our friends.

6. The Old Bakehouse

The Old Bakehouse in Nelson Road in Horsham stands behind number 12, and when a local historian asked me to tell what I know about it I was pleased to agree, as this house and the bakehouse are woven into my earliest and even later memories. I was born in the house in 1931, and later lived there from 1938 to 1975.

Nelson Road and much of the area date from around 1875, much later than the hero it commemorates. From the beginning there were only ten houses along the north side. On the other side of the road were the garden belonging to The Nelson pub (now gone), the entrance to the *cul de sac* of Milton Road (formerly called Prospect Place), and my grandfather's stonemason's yard, part of which he, and later my father also, used as a vegetable garden. All the houses had even numbers. The builder probably intended numbers 10 and 12 to be his *piece de resistance,* as they are a pair, centrally placed, bigger than the rest, and given the decorative flourish of a contrasting yellow brickwork around the windows and front porches. What's more, both properties included a shop window. At least, I know that number 12 had one, and it looks as though number 10 once had one as well, though not in my time. However, at number 10, Bill Aylwin, a soldier from the World War, and his wife ran a small dairy there, and one could buy a bottle of milk by going to a small window at the side of the house and ringing a bell. After the Second War the pair of cottages at the top end of the road and nearest The Nelson were pulled down, and the site used for parking.

My family's association with this part of the Common dates from 1901, when my maternal grandparents moved into Victory Road after my grandfather had finished working as a stonemason on Roedean, the famous girls' school, and set up his own business. Three years later my mother was born. Around the corner in Nelson Road, number 12 was a baker's shop belonging to a Mr and Mrs Reece. My mother, who died in 2001 at nearly 97, recalled that when visiting *her* grandmother in Percy Road, the old lady always gave her as a treat a deep, 'plum-heavy' cake from Reece's for tea. Since 'Granny Gumbrill' died in 1911, the shop and its bakery must have been going strong at that time. Local people were accustomed to taking their cakes round to the bakehouse to be baked in the Reeces' ovens for an 'old penny' or so.

I guess the Reeces died or otherwise gave up around the beginning of the First War, since number 12 was let to a family who came to Horsham from London to avoid any possible war-time bombing. (My mother told me their name, but it escapes for the moment.) The husband worked on *The Morning Post* and travelled to London, surely making him one of Horsham's earliest commuters. There were two daughters, and, with my mother, they attended the Horsham Pupil Teacher Training Centre and Secondary School for Girls, then situated behind the Methodist Church in London Road. (This was the original Horsham High School for Girls.) The family returned to London after the war, and in due course my grandfather bought the property. Although I have the date somewhere I cannot find it, but it must have been around 1925.

The bakehouse, brick-built on two floors, with a slate roof, must be about the same age as the house. My grandfather had the task of pulling out the old ovens. I believe he also put in another window from a job lot he bought when one of the old banks in the Carfax was demolished. Although it would have made a great workshop for his monumental mason's business, I believe he never used it for this, and it became a fine, dry repository for everything that couldn't be found a home anywhere else. At various times it served as a store for fire logs, axes and bill-hooks, coal, our bicycles, cardboard boxes, empty jam jars, garden tools, the stirrup pump (a wartime item), barrels of home-made wine (my grandfather's speciality), vegetables for the kitchen, old newspapers saved as 'salvage', beer by the crate sent up from King & Barnes Brewery, and, in season, the Christmas turkey (hung by the heels from a beam), and anything turfed out of the house that 'might come in'. Water was piped to an ancient stone sink – in which, as a boy, I once discovered Jake, our cat, stretched out, wide-eyed and very dead. (Jake had originally travelled to Horsham in a sack from my father's pre-marital home of Hop Oast Farm, and after that experience Jake never mewed again.) The stone sink at least survives in my present garden planted up with the season's flowers.

The bakehouse upper floor, directly under the slates, always revealed traces of its history as a store for the bakery down below. (It must have been unbearably hot in summer, especially with the ovens going downstairs.) In one corner was built a large wooden receptacle for flour, with a chute for sending it down to the ground floor, while in the middle of the upper floor was a square hole, also presumably used for lifting and lowering raw materials. When I first remember the bakehouse there were wooden steps outdoors leading to a door in the front gable to supply the upper floor, but these steps rotted and were removed, leaving the door opening on to thin air. The only access to the upstairs was then via a vertical wooden ladder nailed to the wall inside the bakehouse and passing through a hole in the ceiling about two feet square. Over about fifty years an unbelievable amount of 'junk' passed through 'the loft', as we called it. Today most of it would fetch a fortune, which makes programmes like *Antiques Roadshow* and *Flog It!* almost unbearable to watch. The oddest thing to come to light when we moved was the primitive dashboard from a T-model Ford that had once belonged to my grandfather.

Number 12 Nelson Road is now divided into two flats, and the present owner of The Old Bakehouse converted and extended it himself to make it into a comfortable residence of some character, where he and his wife are happily living today. But sometimes I dream about the old house and occasionally about the old bakehouse. I am usually back there but somehow know that I shouldn't be because that dear old place is not ours any more. I sometimes wonder whether one day someone will catch sight of me there and swear that the place is haunted. And they will be right, of course.

My School in Flames

On the night of 10TH January 1940 the skies over Horsham glowed an angry red. Four months after the outbreak of the Second World War had German bombers found their way here to set the town alight with their incendiary bombs? Well, actually, no. The glow in the sky was Victory Road Primary School going up in flames, but at the time of the conflagration the nearest German plane was many miles away. When the fire happened the school had been built a mere 38 years, and today Trafalgar School stands on the site.

There were really three single-storied schools in one building – the Infants', the Girls' and the Boys', each with its own walled playground and outside lavatory block behind it. From where we lived it was visible across some gardens and open space, so when it came to the fire I had a grand-stand seat. My acquaintance with the school had begun some four years before the fire when my mother presented me to the kindly and ever behatted Miss Way on my first day. I didn't want to be left, and stood wailing hanging on to my mother with one hand while Miss Way tugged on the other. This upset my mother, who also had a little cry when she got home. While she was doing it a man came to read the meter. 'It's my little boy,' she sobbed. The man was about to offer his condolences on the sad loss of her son, when she came out with her punch line, 'He's just started school!'. Needless to say, I soon liked school and Miss Way so much that I wouldn't come home. I think the day's highlight was always the little bottle of milk (and making bubbles with the straw, of course), five small ginger biscuits and a brief rest period lying on a rush mat.

On the night of the fire my parents woke me up to see the spectacle, and the scene was one I have never forgotten. The building was burning from end to end, with the flames leaping up into the sky and blazing beams crashing down in showers of sparks. But most memorable was the hideous noise, the roaring of the flames and the crashing of roof tiles cascading down into the inferno, glass breaking. The fierce-ness of the fire is hardly surprising, since inside there was an abundance of dry wood – block floors, deal doors and partitions between rooms, all of them pickled in varnish and preservatives. For ages afterwards the smell of destruction by fire hung in the air.

As this was well before the days of personal phones and radios, the police came round to our house to use the telephone (with its number, Horsham 314). It was a bitterly cold night, and after the fire had been put out the sycamore tree at the entrance to the school was hung with long icicles, where the firemen had played their hoses through its branches on to the flames. I am pleased to see that the same sycamore tree still stands sentinel at the gate of the present school.

To continue the children's schooling, makeshift accommodation for the classes had to be found around the town pretty quickly. My class, and I think one other, ended up at the British Legion Clubhouse, situated behind the Ritz Cinema (now the Capitol). No doubt this was arranged through the good offices of the Headmaster, A.H. Eyles, First War veteran and town councillor whose affectionate if unflattering nickname with the boys was 'Hooker' or 'Trunky'. No explanation required. If his cane, (the sort used for discipline, not for walking) had been burnt in the fire he had evidently bought a new one, as it went with him to the Legion Hut. (Caning was only ever on the palm of the open hand.) However, Mr Eyles did once offer me some consolation after I had made a silly mistake. 'Never mind, John,' he said kindly, 'You'll be a man before your mother will.'

There were, indeed still are, two Legion Huts, and we had the use of one of them. They lay close to the railway line with a rough open space between them and the rear of the Ritz, an area now occupied by squash courts. Air raid shelters had been built at Victory Road, but, of course, nothing like that was available in North Street. So they made arrangements for the children to seek shelter in the Ritz in the event of an air raid warning. This was timely, as the war started to hot up and we entered the 'Battle Britain' phase, with warnings frequently going off. Horsham's fire station was just inside the lower gate to Horsham Park, right opposite the Ritz, and this was the site of one of the town's air raid sirens. So we couldn't fail to hear it.

Every time the warning sounded we would run down over the rough ground and along the side of the Ritz, a track covered with king-size flints. If we survived this obstacle course we crept silently into the back row of the stalls and watched whatever film was in progress. At the 'all clear' signal, we trooped out again and back up to the Hut. One day the siren sounded no less than nine times, so in disjointed snippets we eventually saw the whole film. It was called 'North-West Passage' with Spencer Tracy and Robert Young. Later the powers that be decided to send us upstairs in the cinema and for us to sit cross-legged on the floor of the café, so we missed out on the films. In due course the daylight warnings tailed off as Hitler concentrated on night-time raids on London and the big cities. And that's about where my connexion with Victory Road School ran out, because I spent the rest of the war at Collyer's School. There are plenty of stories about that too, but that's probably quite enough of 'the good old days' for now.

Death Drops in on the Rotary **Club**

This 14-instalment story was attached to the Horsham Rotary Club's weekly bulletin when the meetings took place at the Mannings Heath Hotel, which is now under new management and is no longer the venue. All the main characters are fictitious, but the walk-on parts are given the first name of Rotarians at that time.

Part 1 – An Unwelcome Discovery

It was a Thursday evening in early spring with the air becoming chilly. This didn't deter the small group of Rotarians who were chatting outside on the terrace and some enjoying the last cigarette before returning to the bar and then finding the dining room. Something must have caught Big John's eye, as he peered intently towards the lake before saying, very softly, 'O.M.G.!'. Gaby questioned at once, 'What is this O.M.G., John?' Still gazing intently towards the lake John replied, 'It's short for *Oh My God*, Gaby.' Gaby looked towards the lake. 'Yes, it's a nice view, but not exactly new – we've all seen it before.' John didn't reply, but went straight up the steps into the bar, calling out 'Mike, come out here, quickly.' A puzzled Mike came from behind the bar and John muttered a few words to him before both men, looking serious, hurried back outside and across the grass, making for the rushes at the end of the lake. The President and two or three members came to the patio doors to peer into the growing gloom. Sensing that something was amiss, Jeremy and Gordon were soon hard on the heels of the first two. Back in the bar, members continued to chat and to speculate what it was that had made a handful of Rotarians run off into the shadows. Confident that their curiosity would soon be satisfied, and not caring much either way, the rest of the gathering remained warm and comfortable and found time to refresh their drinks.

No one had come back indoors, so it remains a mystery how the words 'a body' immediately seemed to be on everyone's lips. Perhaps someone had made a light-hearted joke, not for a moment thinking that they could be speaking the truth. Yet speaking the truth they were. Down by the lake Mike had called an ambulance on his mobile, though he felt confident that whenever it arrived it would be too late. Jeremy and Gordon had volunteered to stay down by the lake with 'it', whatever 'it' was. On getting back to the bar, John announced to all and sundry in a matter-of-fact tone, 'There's a body down there.' A Rotarian asked, 'Is it a member?' 'Don't think, so,' said John, 'it's kinda half in and half out of the water, but it's fully dressed. There's not a lot of light down there.' Someone said, 'Why didn't you pull him out of the water? He could still be alive.' Mike was on the house phone, but with one hand pushed a large Scotch across the counter to John. 'He might still be alive, you think?' someone asked. 'Well,' said John, 'somehow I don't think so. You see, he, or she, doesn't have a head.' And with that, John took a hearty swig from the whisky glass, and the whole gathering fell silent.

(To be continued...)

Part 2 – Well, who was it?

Discovering a body beside the lake was not an auspicious start for what should have been a normal meeting of the Rotary Club. Eventually everyone went into the dining room, but there was only one topic of conversation. The ambulance and two police cars turned up quite quickly and all tried to get into the top car park at the same time. Eventually they were sent down to the lower entrance, and we could see their lights as they bumped across the grass towards the lake. John and the other members who had actually seen the body stayed out in the bar talking to a policeman and describing what they had seen when they had run to the lake. It was an evening for a speaker, a young school teacher who specialized in playing the nose flute. She had brought several with her, from various parts of the world, and went through her repertoire, playing each one and showing slides of nose-flute players dressed in their traditional costumes. She was a sweet girl, 'fragrant' a judge might say, and in normal times members would have made a big fuss of her, but tonight even those who visibly melt in the presence of pretty girls could not get the earlier events of the evening out of their minds. Maybe it wasn't the body of a man down there. For all anyone knew, it could have been a woman. It could have been someone we all knew, perhaps someone we saw every week at a meeting.

After the ambulance had left, Jeremy and Gordon returned to the meeting. They said the body was that of a man, according to the paramedics probably around his mid-twenties, which at once ruled out the possibility that he was indeed a member of the Club. At this stage there was no means of identifying him further, and an autopsy and search of police records would all take time. The lack of a head was a distinct disadvantage in putting a name to the unfortunate gatecrasher. A contact in the media later confessed to John that he was sorry the body wasn't a woman and he could run with the headline *Lady in the Lake – headless woman drops in on Rotarians.* Maybe he would have to fall back on *Did stag-night horseplay go too far? Next day, sober-suited Rotarians find guest who lost his head and refused to go home after forest frolics.*...But it wasn't to be either of them.

(To be continued...)

Part 3 – Rotarians Questioned

The local paper was a disappointment when it appeared on the following Thursday. It was known that a reporter had interviewed some of the members about finding the body beside the lake, and that the journalist had intended to make it front page news. When it came to it, the lead story was nothing to do with the body but was all about someone setting fire to a garden shed in Jenger's Mead and singeing the tail of a she cat that had gone there to have kittens. There was also a large colour photo of flowers that people had laid at the scene in tribute to a neonate kitten that had un-fortunately 'perished in the inferno'. Eventually someone found an item on page 2 to the effect that police were investigating the unexplained death of a man in Mannings

Heath. And that's all.

This was a Business Meeting, and Rotarians had said grace and sat down and the girls were bringing in the soup. Then one of them approached the President in mid-spoonful and said there was someone outside to see him, so he went out. There were three people, led by a thirtyish blonde wearing a grey tailored suit and cherry-coloured scarf at the neck. Behind her was a stocky guy wearing a roll-neck sweater, black trousers and a black leather jacket. The third was an older man in a suit, white shirt and stripy tie. They all produced ID cards, all different but all bearing the royal insignia. The woman's card bore a diagonal red stripe. She didn't waste her words, 'We'd like to speak to your members about what happened last week, especially those who saw the body. We'd also like the details of everyone else here, and to know when we can speak to people not here this week but who were present last Thursday.' The three unexpected visitors commandeered the small tables in the bar, and members were called from the dining room three at a time to be interviewed by the trio. After a curt 'thank-you' the three left in three cars as quickly as they had appeared, leaving members to speculate on the meeting's surprise business. No one could agree on what was written on the id-cards they had seen. Some were convinced it was 'Home Office', others 'Foreign and Commonwealth Office' while the sweater man just had a scrawled signature, a phone number and a 'box number', but no one could remember whether it was 'Box 50' or 'Box 500'.

When John asked someone at the local paper why they

had pulled the original story, he simply said, 'No idea. It came from higher up. You'll have to ask the haggis-bashers. Anyway, it's all blood under the bridge now. Can't stop. Someone's been letting down the tyres of kids' bikes parked outside a school in Roffey, and we've got a great pic of out-raged mums holding up the same placards in protest. Only the silly cows miss-spelt half of the words. So bang goes Roffey's bid for Village of Culture in three years' time!'

(To be continued...)

Part 4 – George Hall

Rotarians came to the conclusion that there must have been what's called 'a news blackout' on anything concerning the body found in the lake. Soon afterwards Horsham Rotarian Dennis Bagshawe ran into one George Hall in the bar at the Mannings Heath Golf Club. Hall was a freelance journalist of dubious reputation. The two of them watched while golfers ran back up to the clubhouse as the rain hammered down, and after a couple of *Becks* they started talking about the strange event at the Rotary meeting. The journalist had once worked on the *News of the World*, so being used to sail-ing close to the wind he said he'd sniff around a bit to see what was 'going down' about it in Wapping. Since the local paper had nothing on it, understandably nothing had found its way to the nationals either. Having said cheerio to Dennis, who was expected home for lunch, George Hall ordered another *Becks* and settled down to do some phoning. He always carried at least three state-of-the-art smart phones and regularly changed their numbers to cover his tracks. Masquerading as someone official, his first call was to the mortuary at the East Surrey Hospital to enquire whether there were any results yet from the Mannings Heath post mortem. After a bit of keyboard clicking and paper shuffling the answer came that the body had never gone there. They had been expecting it, but it never turned up. His next call was to Freeman Brothers to see if the body had finished up in their chapel of rest. No, he wasn't there either. A trawl of other funeral firms in the area produced the same answer. At this point George Hall came over all sleepy and dozed off, waking up again about six o'clock and judging this the ideal time to sink his first pink gin of the evening, a pick-me-up he had favoured since once being attached to the Royal Navy as public relations officer at the M.O.D. By the time came for him to walk back home to his cottage in the village he had completely forgotten about his quest to track down the whereabouts of the mystery body.

Next morning Hall was just sinking his second *Becks* at the clubhouse when his conversation with the Rotarian the day before suddenly came back to him. What he really needed was an interview with the paramedics who had turned up with the police on that Thursday evening. They were eyewitnesses of whoever it was had been pulled out of the lake. It took a lot of phone calls and a good deal of impersonation, but he eventually ended up with the names of both of the paramedics, Kevin and Sam, and he was more than pleased when he discovered that the 'Sam' was a Samantha. So, unconsciously adjusting his Calvin Klein

Y-fronts, George settled down to getting an interview from Sam, and, with luck, maybe a bit more.

(To be continued....)

Part 5 – Paramedics in Demand

When Sam came downstairs Mandy was already up and dressed and just going out to get her *Sun*. Mandy worked at a twenty-four hour call centre, and today their shifts had happened to coincide. Later Sam put her head in her hands and looked at Mandy, 'What am I going to do about this old nuisance who keeps ringing me about that body we picked up at Mannings Heath? He keeps ringing and texting, but God know how he got my number.'

Mandy was concentrating on *Sun* gossip about Jordan. 'Don't ask me. Just don't answer. Just tell him to piss off. I'll speak to him for you if you like.'

'He wants to see me. He says he'll pay me for an interview. Could be quite big money, he reckons.'

'Well, it's up to you. He's probably just a dirty old man and wants to try it on. However old they are, some of them never give up. I expect you'll find he's well old, like forty or even fifty or something. Anyway, you're not supposed to go round blabbing about patients to reporters, are you?'

'The dead guy wasn't exactly a patient was he? All I know is there was nothing where his head should have been. I didn't look too closely. He was my first one of those I've had, and it turned me up a bit. I suppose I'll get used to it.'

'Tell him anything, just to get him off your back.'

'Well,' said Sam, 'besides the head thing, he did look pretty smashed up. Like he'd fallen off a skyscraper or something. Loads of fractures and stuff I should think. Then there was that business of us being pulled over by the police on the way to the East Surrey and having to transfer the guy to this big car. At the front end it looked like one of those really big BMWs, but the back end was more like a funeral car, a hearse with black windows. I swear there was room for half a dozen bodies in the back of that thing, three shelves on each side. And the men did look more like undertakers.'

'Sounds pretty spooky,' observed Mandy, 'I hate that sort of thing.'

'And,' remembered Sam, 'Kevin made a bit of a joke and said to them, "Sorry, there's no head," and the old guy who was the driver said something very funny. He said, "Don't worry. We've already got his head." And the younger guy looked as mad as hell and said "Shut up. Shut UP!" Then they drove off, no green form or anything. The younger guy sounded pretty posh, but the driver was from London. I bet that's where they were going.'

Mandy was still flicking through her *Sun*. 'I see they reckon *You've Been Framed* is a set-up. People make their kids fall off swings, walk into doors and get trampled by ponies just for the laughs. Isn't that awful?'

But Sam wasn't listening. 'I know. I'll ask Kevin if the reporter guy has been ringing him. After all, Kevin's my team leader and he knows more about it than I do. He'll know what to do.'

(To be continued...)

136

Part 6 – George Hall shows his cloven hoof

When George Hall walked into the bar at the Golf Club he found the Rotarian he had met there before. George Hall brought his drink over.

'Mind if I join you?' 'Be my guest,' replied Rotarian Dennis, 'then you can tell me if you found out anything about the body that we discovered by the lake a few Thursdays ago.'

George killed half his *Becks* at one gulp. 'First today,' George confided, 'No, I tell a lie. I had a wee gin after breakfast to take way the taste of the orange juice. I made a bit of progress on your John Doe.'

The Rotarian leant forward, 'Tell me more'.

'Well,' said George, 'that paramedic woman, Sam, was a dead loss, wouldn't say a word, a right little tight-arse. I kept ringing her trying to get her to talk, but no dice. Then I had a stroke of luck. She spoke to her team leader, a bloke called Kevin, and she asked him what she should do. He said she was quite right to consult him. He's obviously a devious bastard – takes one to know one – so he asked her for my number and he was on to me like a shot. Wanted to know how much would be in it for him if he spilled the beans about the stiff that turned up at your Rotary meeting.'

'So what's the story?' enquired Dennis.

'Well, it's really only half a story at the moment. The paramedics thought the guy looked a bit worse for wear, as though he may have jumped off the Post Office Tower or something. Did he fall or was he helped on his way? And it seems that the police highjacked the ambulance on the way to the East Surrey and transferred him into some sort of undertaker's meat wagon before speeding off in a northerly direction, probably up to The Smoke. There was a small gold name on the car's door, something like *Waverton*. I shall have to work on that. And whoever they are, the highjackers may already have his head. So how did they get hold of that? It must have come off before he got to the lake, so how did that happen? And whoever got the police to play up must have some hefty clout or knows what a bloody good bung looks like.'

'A bung?'

'Yes, yes,' said George, getting impatient, 'A bung – a bloody wedge! I've handed out a few in my time. I expect you have too, old boy. You were in business, weren't you?'

The Rotarian looked stern. 'Not that sort of business, my friend.'

'Oh well, please yourself,' said George, already wondering whether he had said too much and given too much of his story away to a stranger, who, maybe, wasn't quite on his wavelength after all.

'Oh, what the hell,' said George, 'how about another **Becks**?'

'That's very kind, but I really must go. I'm auditing the Scouts' accounts and must finish them by tomorrow.' With that, Dennis left.

(To be continued…)

Part 7 – Piecing it together

As Dennis drove home from the Golf Club he started to have misgivings about his acquaintance, George. In some ways he was an interesting guy, but a very different kettle of fish from his usual friends, and quite unlike members of the Rotary Club. He was a boozer, a bit of a chancer and given to colourful language, and maybe it was his sheer difference that made him interesting. Yes, George was definitely 'a bit of a bounder'.

But George had said one thing that made Dennis think hard. Apparently that odd hearse-type vehicle that had picked up the body on the Crawley road had a tiny name like *Waverton* painted on its door. Dennis just happened to know that *Wavertons* were the really classy firm of undertakers in London, who had stylishly conveyed the great and the good to their eternal rest for generations, and were still doing so. So whoever it was they had snatched from the paramedics he was unlikely to be put six feet under in a box knocked up out of MDF.

Dennis had missed the meeting when the body had been found at Mannings Heath, but he had later been interviewed by someone in plain clothes. He seemed a decent enough chap around fiftyish wearing a tweed sports jacket, nondescript trousers. It transpired that he was a retired police superintendent who normally went round the country doing security vettings on civil servants and others hoping to progress to a higher clearance level. Apparently, the three who had interviewed members of the Club about the fateful Thursday evening had been tight-lipped, and Dennis was surprised that his own interrogator had disclosed anything at all about himself. On impulse Dennis remarked, 'They say he looked as though he had fallen from a high building, like the post office tower.' His questioner grimaced, 'Well, Mr. Bagshawe, there aren't many post office towers round this part of Surrey, pardon me, Sussex isn't it, and there are other ways of getting all smashed up. You could be duffed up in a dark alley, or you could fall out of a plane. The result would be much the same.'

After his visitor had gone, Dennis thought about his words. They had said there were no signs of a struggle at Mannings Heath and not many dark alleys there either. And nothing indicated that the body had been dragged across the turf of the greens to end up on the edge of the lake. Dennis slowly came to the conclusion that the powers that be believed that the headless visitor had been encouraged to exit from a passing aircraft.

(To be continued)

Part 8 – Justine Vachell

It was about a week since Dennis Bagshawe's last encounter with George Hall the boozy journalist. Jo Bagshawe had been running round getting ready to drive to an Inner Wheel District lunch meeting at Leatherhead, and after showing Dennis what he should have for his lunch she finally exited, trailing a miasma of Bulgari *Mon Jasmin Noir* behind her through the house. Dennis relaxed and prepared just to potter around, happy to know that he would have the place entirely to himself for most of the day – read the paper, a drink, lunch, and then a spot of Channel Four racing from Sandown Park. Perfect! Then the phone rang. The voice was female and foreign.

'Hallo, hallo, is that Mr. Bagshawe, the Secretary of the Rotarian people at Horsham in Sussex?'

'Well, I was the secretary once,' said Dennis, 'many years ago.'

'Ah, good,' said the voice. 'Can you help me? I want to see the place where the young man was found, where the Rotarian members meet. For only a few days I am in England. Please... it is important to me.'

It took Dennis a few seconds to sort out his thoughts. 'Who are you, and where are you speaking from?'

'My name is Justine Vachell, and I am at the London Gatwick airport. I am at Europcar desk for a car. I drive in Paris all the time and I have driven before in U.K. and can come to your Rotarian office in Sussex. As you say, *no sweat*.'

'Hold your horses,' blurted Dennis, becoming more perturbed by the minute. 'The place is not an office, it's just a hotel where the members meet.'

'OK, I know this horses expression, but I must go there, I must! You see, he was my boy Louis, my son, and I must see where he fell to the earth. He was a good boy, and loved the planes, but he was so daring and would take so many of the risks. When the engines were going round he would just walk up to them like on the promenade, but those propellers, they are so dangerous. You must not go close to

141

them, or you have a most bad accident. But his friends were bad people, with the drugs and bad things. I had money from his father to care for him, but the boy would go where he should not. The children are coming out from us, but they will never listen to what we say. They must always do something different, never what we tell them.'

Dennis saw his planned day receding rapidly. It took about half an hour to explain to Justine Vachell how she should find Mannings Heath from Gatwick, and was certain that by the end of it she had understood less than half. It would have been much easier to have just referred her to the club's President. But that would have been selfish, and, after all, even Dennis was not immune to the allure of female tones with an intriguing accent. So he set out to meet Justine at Mannings Heath Hotel.

(To be continued...)

Part 9 – Justine views the lake

Dennis realized that in the space of a short phone call the woman had told him quite a lot, either directly or at least by implication. The body in the lake had evidently been this woman's son, and he had probably fallen from an aircraft flying over Mannings Heath. As she was French, the plane had probably taken off from somewhere in Northern France. Her anxiety about walking close to planes with propellers probably pointed to the cause of his death and explained why the corpse was headless. After all, a fast-moving propeller would make a most effective guillotine. The reference to the young man's friends and to drugs explained the reason for a trip to England that had probably gone badly wrong. Dennis imagined a group of young men in France seeing their friend decapitated by a small plane's propeller, and then at their wits' end to know what to do next. So they bundled the corpse into the plane and took off, more or less sticking to their original flight plan to land at Gatwick or some field in Sussex or Surrey. Around Mannings Heath the pilot lost his nerve and someone pushed the body out of the aircraft. Dennis pondered to himself whether his imagination had run away with him, or whether the real story was close to his scenario.

Dennis had allowed Justine an hour to reach Mannings Heath, confident that it would take her much longer than that to arrive there and hoping that he could grab some lunch to make up for missing Jo's offering. So he was surprised to see a woman sitting on a bar stool drinking orange juice. It had to be Justine, wearing a lavender corded silk *kepi* and pink linen trouser suit. Dennis guessed that she was somewhere around forty-five years old. Looking past Justine's slightly sagging jaw line and early wrinkles Dennis detected the signs of a once stunningly good looking mademoiselle and still not a gramme overweight. She proffered a braceleted hand to Dennis and remained seated on her perch, in no hurry to drain her orange juice.

Eventually she gave Dennis a quizzical scrutiny. 'Well, Monsieur Dennis, what can you tell me or show me?' Rotarian Dennis suspected that there was little that he could

143

tell a woman like Justine.

'Well, Madame Vachell, all I can do is to show you where your son met with his most tragic accident, down by the lake. We here know very little about it.' Justine picked up her Chanel clutch bag from the bar and slid down off the stool in one easy move. 'O.K.,' she said, '*marchons*', and took Dennis's arm and steered him towards the patio as though she already knew the way out to the lake. As they left, behind the bar Mike gave Wendy a puzzled look and they both shrugged. As Dennis and Justine approached the lake, Dennis caught sight of a red Audi leaving the car park. It was George Hall's car. Driven erratically, of course.

(To be continued...)

Part 10 – George Hall offends Dennis

Dennis didn't know what to make of Justine. She spent only a few minutes contemplating the lake behind the hotel, then, thanking Dennis extravagantly for his trouble, she was back to her hire car and was on her way, without saying where she was going or what she was intending to do. Was she staying somewhere over night or would she be on her way back to Paris? And what had George Hall been doing in the car park and roaring away as soon as he and Justine walked out on to the patio? Dennis thought it would all make a good story to tell Jo when she came back from her District Meeting at Leatherhead, but when she started scolding him for apparently forgetting to cook his lunch, he thought he would put her straight about it tomorrow. And these goings-on with Justine seemed so strange that he felt that she might pop up again somewhere, with or without her jaunty little Gallic headgear. Well, in that case he would have more to tell Jo when the time came – wouldn't he? But that night Dennis actually dreamt about Justine, and it was nice. Actually, rather too nice. He decided that it would be best not to tell Jo about *that*.

Next morning Jo and a few girl friends had arranged to have the day in London. Every so often they went up on the train and lunched together at somewhere 'rather swish'. Today they were raiding Fortnum's and would either stay there for lunch on the top floor, or move on to *Gordon Ramsay at Claridge's*, and in no time one of her chums was picking her up to catch the train from Horsham, so Dennis would see very little of Jo that day. As he was still baffled by recent events, Dennis thought he would go down to the Golf Club on the chance of running into Hall. To his surprise he found him at a table in the bar and on one of his many phones. As soon as he saw Dennis he rang off. His welcome was not over-friendly.

'Hello, whad'you want, my Rotarian friend? Full of good bloody works?'

'Did I see you at the hotel yesterday?' Dennis enquired.

'You know bloody well you did. Well, what did she tell you?'

'Who? You mean the French lady?'

'Oh, come on,' said Hall, 'you know what I'm talking about. If you spoil my story I'll bloody kill you. No. I'll screw you first, then I'll bloody kill you. In a few days every

145

paper in the world will be carrying my story.'

Dennis stood up. 'I've no idea what you're talking about, but I do know you are odious and offensive. I'm amazed they allowed you to join this club.'

'Well, I'll tell you something,' sneered Hall, 'I'm not a member of this bloody club. I only drink here because the beer's cheaper than South bloody Lodge. And I'll tell you something else – if certain guys in higher places than you could just keep it in their trousers when visiting *rue du Fuckin Faubourg St Honoré*, there would be no story and I wouldn't be wasting my time talking to a prissy old fart like you, Dennis bloody Bagwash.'

(To be continued…)

Part 11 – An Unsettling Day for Dennis

Dennis had been shaken by Hall's outburst, and went straight back to the empty house and poured himself a large glass of *Bristol Cream*. (Why on earth did Jo insist on putting empty gin bottles back into the drinks cupboard?) Apart from his offensive words, which Dennis had understood only too well, what on earth was the boozy blighter talking about? High-placed guys keeping their trousers on in the *rue something or other*? What was all that? Of course, there was a common denominator somewhere, and it must have something to do with Justine Vachell who had come from Paris. From what she had said on the phone, she evidently thought that the young man in the lake had been her son Louis, and that someone had pushed his body out

146

of a plane. Dennis felt he should tell the police, until he realized that the police already knew about the incident and had even questioned all the members of the Rotary Club, including himself. At a loss to know quite what to do next, Dennis went to his car and to gather his thoughts decided to drive around for a bit. St.Leonard's Forest was always welcoming at this time of year, with all its trees coming out in their many shades of green. He pulled up and sat beside the end of Roost Hole Pond, a couple of motionless fisherman on the distant bank. Eventually he felt he should go home, so set off slowly for the village. Then it dawned on him that he would be passing George Hall's cottage. Sure enough, there in the driveway was his red Audi, but behind it was another car. It was a new blue Astra, with a Europcar sticker in the rear window. There was only one person the driver might be.

About five o'clock Jo came back from her trip to London. She said her new Jimmy Choos were killing her, but always swore she hadn't bought them too small. And London had given her a headache. This was nothing new. London always gave Jo a headache.

'Where did you have lunch in the end?' enquired Dennis.

'Oh, Gordon Ramsay's,' said Jo.

'Was it O.K.?' asked Dennis.

Jo fell back into a chair. 'Yeah, not bad.' Then, as an afterthought, 'Gorgeous wine waiter – coloured boy – nice bum. I'm going for a shower.'

Dennis gave Jo a half an hour, then called out, 'Are you

doing anything for supper?' to which Jo called back 'God, I'm not up to supper. Go and pick up a Chinese or something for yourself if you're hungry. I'm going to bed. You can bring a coffee in to me tomorrow morning about ten, if you can remember it.'

On the way back from picking up his supper Dennis thought he would drive by George Hall's cottage again. The Audi was still there. But there was no sign of the Astra.

(To be continued.)

Part 12 – So near yet...

Had Dennis Bagshawe been passing George Hall's cottage around nine o'clock the next morning instead of brewing Jo's coffee, he would have seen Hall taking a light set of aluminium steps from his garage and, with difficulty, getting them into the Audi. Eventually satisfied, he turned his attention to setting the satnav. It was some time since he had been to Windsor. Traffic was heavy all along the route, but eventually he negotiated his way along the High Street and then into Park Street. He pulled his car into a layby which gave him a good view of the Long Walk and the entrance to Frogmore and the burial ground. Hall was checking over his cameras with long lenses when a couple of soberly dressed men appeared from a lodge and opened the iron gates. At the same time two police motorcyclists drove up to the open gates and parked across the roadway, so that although the way was now open, there was still no access. Hall knew that the moment he had been waiting for had almost arrived. The scoop of the century was now very close.

In the rear-view mirror Hall could see the approaching cars, and in a moment the small convoy of a police car (no blue flashing light), three Range Rovers with dark windows followed by a blue Astra had shot past him and through the open gates. The motorcyclists then resumed their station blocking the road. This was Hall's signal to start the car and drive out of sight of the policemen and down a bridle path that ran parallel with the high stone wall surrounding the Frogmore estate and Windsor Great Park. When he came to an iron gate in the wall used exclusively by the estate gardeners he pulled up. From here he could just see the green top of the Victoria and Albert Mausoleum, and nearby an exclusive burial ground dominated here and there by giant marble angels and crosses. And there, to one side, was a line of cars and a dark knot of people beginning to gather in one particular place. Hall hastily extricated his aluminium steps from the car, and with both cameras slung around his neck mounted his vantage point. With a good view through his telephotos he needed no binoculars to bring the tableau into view. Among the group he could easily discern the splash of a white clerical surplice, but accurate identification would have to await enlargement of the very high-resolution images. Accurate identification of key figures in the group could make a difference of thousands of pounds to the value of his copyright. Hall found that his hand was shaking so much that the cameras were all over the place. For such an event he had brought a flask of neat vodka. He struggled to extricate it from a pocket and removed the silver top, which he promptly dropped into the grass under his steps. 'Bugger, bugger...' He never reached his third 'bugger'. At this moment he lost his balance and fell from the steps, striking his head on the iron gatepost, landing heavily on the hardened mud left by the gardeners' tractors.

(To be continued...)

Part 13 – News of a death

Some days after Dennis had been disgusted by George Hall's outburst at the Golf Club he was still baffled by the turn of events. What had an attractive woman like Justine Vachell been doing at Hall's cottage two nights ago? Had they known each other all along, or had Hall contacted Justine after her arrival at Mannings Heath? And if the body in the lake had really been her son, Louis, Hall thought there was a big news story in the tragedy. That morning Dennis decided to get the mower out and to ready it for the first cut of spring. Meanwhile, Jo took her car down to the Village Store to pick up some much-needed groceries and a fresh bottle of Beefeater. When she came back she called out to Dennis. 'Guess what I've just heard. That reporter guy who you say goes to the Golf Club is dead. You knew him a bit, didn't you?'

Dennis went indoors and attempted to find something about George Hall on the Internet. Later he joined Jo in the kitchen, 'Well I'm damned. It's true enough. There's something on the net about him. Apparently he'd gone to Windsor and was trying to photograph something the other side of a high wall and fell off those steps they carry around. They think he must have hit his head, but there'll be a post mortem, of course. What can he have been doing there? They say he was born in South Africa and that he was 55. Full name George Woodhouse Hall. He was sacked from the *News of the World* about three years ago for unethical journalistic practices.'

Jo busied herself putting away the shopping. 'Thanks a bundle for that information, Dennis. Absolutely fascinating news. You really come out with some riveting stuff sometimes. I don't know how you do it.' (Not for the first time Dennis observed wryly to himself that Jo had majored in Irony.)

Dennis picked up the red top of the Beefeater bottle from the floor where Jo had left it, and, observing her holding her glass close to her chest with both hands, guessed that lunch may be a little late, so he went back into the study to see if he had any emails. He had completely forgotten that Justine had asked for his email address until it came up on the screen.

Cher Dennis

I want to thank you so much for the help you gave me when I came to England. It was sad for me to see where my Louis fell, but now he is at rest.

I did not like at all a Monsieur Hall who found me and tried to make me tell him things. But I trust you, and will tell you, Dennis. He thought my poor Louis would make him a big fortune, and much trouble for some other people. I now have a job again at r.d. F. St.H. It is like the old times.

Let me show you Paris one day soon. St Denis is our *patron*, you know! Justine

Dennis swallowed hard and stared at the screen until Jo declared the two *Bird's-Eye Dinners* would not be ready yet because she had forgotten to switch the oven on.

(To be continued)

Part 14 – The rewards of silence

As week succeeded week, Rotarians and everyone else had almost forgotten the Thursday night when a young teacher had come to demonstrate the nose flute to the Club, and the same evening the corpse of a young man had been found in the lake. Nothing about this had appeared in the news media, but it was known that not long afterwards a French woman had contacted Dennis Bagshawe, and that he had shown her the lake to view the spot where, she said, her son had fallen from an aircraft. Dennis was later asked to say a few words to the Club about it, but he declined, declaring that he knew no more about it than anyone else. Dennis had considered it unnecessary to pass on anything that Justine had told him about Louis and his accident. The appearance of interrogators to ask questions about the event was never explained, and the memory of it faded. If the late George Hall had made any discoveries and passed them on to Dennis, then Dennis must have decided they were best forgotten. After all, wasn't the man a bounder and blotto for most of the time? When the New Year Honours came out everyone in the Rotary Club was staggered when the name Dennis Cyril Bagshawe appeared on the list as being made an Officer of the Most Excellent Order of the British Empire for public service. After all, what had Dennis ever done that was so special? Nothing that anyone could think of. No one had noticed that in the same Honours List the name Justine Chantal Vachell appeared in the overseas section of honorary honours.

Talk of France had encouraged Dennis to brush up his conversational French, and to become quite interested in French art and culture. Jo had put it all down to Dennis watching a series on the Palace of Versailles and various arty programmes on BBC4. He even became a member of the *Société des Amis du Louvre*, so that he could pop over to attend special exhibitions and cultural events in Paris. The Tunnel had brought Paris much closer, so he could get over and back in the day. Dennis always asked Jo if she would like to come with him on these cultural jaunts, but Jo declared that if she was that bored she'd rather stick pins into her eyes for entertainment.

Not long after the announcements Dennis informed Jo there was a special exhibition in Paris that he said he greatly wanted to see, so he would pop over, just for the day. Shortly after this, Justine was entertaining a friend to lunch in her apartment to celebrate her English honour. Her companion was also in a celebratory mood, and as they raised their glasses Justine's guest allowed himself an enigmatic smile, like the Mona Lisa, which they had now seen several times together at the Louvre, just down the road. After all, weren't they now both *amis*, and celebrating because, thanks to the two of them, to the world at large the Rotary Mystery was likely to remain just that?

(End/fin)

After Wayne

Transcription of a contribution by 'Mary Brandon'

With thanks to the 'How We Live Today' Social Audit Group, Social Studies Faculty of the Pennine-Peaks College of Further Education (P-PCFE)

To preserve anonymity all names are changed.

Mary dictates:

Hope this is working.

When Wayne walked out on me I wasn't expecting it. Well, I didn't have any reason. He was always fiddling with his phone and going out quite a bit, mostly down 'The Queens', and I didn't mind because, to be honest, once the boys were born it was easier when he wasn't here. Our house is quite small, and mostly he just hung around waiting for me to stick a plate of food in front of him. And I was quite pleased, in a way, when he stopped bothering me at bedtime. Things used to be OK, but after the babbies came we seemed to lose interest. I can live without it. Anyway, he was always a bit rough.

Of course, there's plenty of women at Mason's where Wayne worked. He took the stuff in to them with his fork truck where they're all sitting filling these boxes with screws and nuts and stuff. Some of them are just kids out of school, skirts right up to their backsides and ready with plenty of backchat with anything in trousers. Some of the older ones are just as bad. Someone said there's places they go, this room where they chuck all the reject boxes for recycling, and it's quite cosy. They can even turn the key on the inside. If anyone's missing, someone says they've gone to the toilet or on the phone or some garbage like that. Most of the supervisors are so dozy they'd never know anyway. My friend said half the foremen are at it, and the women think they'll have it easy if they keep on the right side of the foremen and there's nearly always one or other of them in there for a blow job or something.

One night Wayne never came home from work, and I was just getting worried and one of his mates rings up. Message from Wayne. He won't be home tonight, he's never coming home again. He's found someone else. And he's chucked up Mason's. I was gobsmacked. Getting one of his mates to ring me. He didn't even have the guts to tell me himself. I admit, I had a cry, but I was more angry than anything. Then I went upstairs. All his stuff was gone, all his clothes, the Halifax book, everything. God knows how he got it all out of the house without me seeing. And of course he'd taken the car, so he had that as well – not that I can drive, anyway. Dad wouldn't let me learn until I was older, and once we were married we could only afford one car. When the message had sunk in, I rang the mate who'd told me. He said he didn't know who she was or where they'd gone. The worst thing was when Wolf and Red kept asking where their Dad was. And they cried when they went to bed. And I cried as well.

When I told Mum she said she'd never liked Wayne anyway, and it was a good job that Dad was already gone, as the shock of would have killed him. Dad had quite liked him at first, and just after we were married he used to take Wayne down the Legion, but that dropped off after a time, well Dad's legs got bad so he couldn't get out. Poor old Dad. I told the police and the Salvoes that Wayne was missing, but they soon sized it up – he'd just done a bunk. She has to be one of the women from Mason's. I thought that Mason's would be mad at them just walking out like that, but they're such a shambles down there what with people walking in and out they likely never even noticed. Oh, and the day he went he emptied the Halifax account, every penny of it. It wasn't much anyway, just the little bit what I'd saved when I was working before I met Wayne. We were supposed to be buying the house. So when he went I just had to get a job. I was going for one anyway as soon as the twins started school, but I've had to work now and take the kids down the road to the childminding woman, Susie.

I stick both the kids in the double buggy and push them down Bronte Street, then round into Dales Road. It takes me about ten minutes going, but longer coming back, as it's all uphill. They've been doing up one of the houses in Bronte Street, and there's been a skip outside. A lot of the old people who used to live down there are popping off and younger ones are coming in. I think some of them have done up the houses themselves. But it's a proper builder doing the one with the skip, number 63. They've painted it bright red all over, brickwork, all of it. Then the curtains went up, purple with big yellow spots. The new people in there haven't put up any nets. Most of them round here have nets, as they're afraid of people looking in on them. We've, I've, got nets myself, but they do make the front room a bit dark.

Couple of weeks ago when I was pushing the kids past number 63 I got a bit of a shock, as when I looked up there was this big old Indian guy with big white whiskers standing in the bay window looking out. He never moved and I thought he was a sort of waxwork. He had a white shirt and white trousers. The kids never saw him as they were scrapping. When I came by again he'd gone. Next morning, there he was again in the window. I tried not to notice him, but the boys saw him this time but they never said anything. Sometimes they point at people and call out things like 'Funny old man'. They don't mean anything by it, they just come out with what's in their head. They make me curl up sometimes. I did wonder if the old man was going to do something, something nasty, you know, like open his trousers kind of thing. That's why I tried not to look at him. But he didn't. I could always cross over and go down the other side of Bronte Street, but if I do that I've only got to cross back again when I get to the bottom.

Next time I go by, the kids see him again, and blow me they both wave to him, and the old Indian bloke smiles and waves back. I could have died. If they hadn't been in the buggy I'd have clouted them both, as I've always told them never to do that sort of thing. And at that age you can't explain it, can you? They'll find out soon enough as it is. Expect he's harmless, but you can't take chances. After a bit the boys got tired of waving. Most of the time they're too busy arguing and punching each other about. They drive me mad, I could bang their heads together or tip them in the cut. Expect that now people will say it's because they've got no dad, but he never lifted a finger when they played up. If it was up to him they'd just run wild like animals. Well, I don't suppose he'll have any kids with his fancy woman, he'll be too careful for that. They'll be swanning about spending my money. Someone saw them in the precinct the other day, so they can't have gone far. They said she looks quite young, and pretty, sod her.

The old Indian guy has started waving at me now when we go by. I blanked him at first, but he seems to have quite a nice face, so I started to give him a little wave back. I couldn't see the harm in it, though Mum would create if she knew. I've never seen his old woman. Maybe he lives on his own. If he does, he must cook for himself, as there's quite a stink of curry round there. I quite like a curry. I've never made it at home, but Wayne and me had a takeaway sometimes of a Saturday tea when I didn't want to bother with sausages. Wayne would live on sausages – and burgers.

When Mum came round she said she'd seen Wayne too, but without his tart. And, would you believe, he was pushing a kid in a chair, a boy, no older than my two. Mum said it looked white-faced, like it was frozen. It can't be theirs. Unless it *is* theirs, and he's been giving it to her for yonks. No, someone would have told me. Still, you can't help wondering. Mum said Wayne looked a bit rough himself. He saw her coming, and was in such a hurry to cross the road to miss her that he nearly shot the kid out of the pushchair.

159

Later on, going down Bronte Street, there was a police car down near number 63. There's always a few cars down there as there's no garages, same as my place. So I wasn't sure where the coppers had gone. Could have been into the old man's. Anyway, when I came back after picking up the kids there was this plain white van outside 63, and I sussed it. It belongs to Thrupps and I recognized the two guys with it, as they were the same ones who came to collect Dad when he died. Just as I got there they were bringing out this battered old brown coffin, no proper handles. They made a bit of a song getting it through the front door and down the steps. It must have been the old Indian bloke. I don't know why really, but I was a quite upset. I rang Mum after tea and told her, but she didn't want to know as she was all steamed up and carrying on about next door's pigeons crapping down her washing.

Not long after the old man died they put up a sale board. He hadn't been there long, and doing it up must have cost him a bomb. I wondered whether I would see him standing in the window again, like his spirit or ghost kind of thing, and then he'd just vanish or something. Of course, I never saw him. But about that time, when I was late and tearing down Bronte Street with the twins, just as we were passing number 63, Red shouts 'Stop' and Wolf points at the window and laughs and says 'Funny man'. It was dead creepy. There was no one there. So I gave them both a good clip round the ear and carried on down the hill. Like I said, it was scary. And I wanted to tell someone about it, but Mum won't want to know.

It's got like that now with Mum and nextdoor's pigeons and their mess that she bangs on and on about them every time I see her. I can't blame her, but I just wish she wouldn't keep rabbiting on about them. The old man next door is a funny old bugger, and as bolshy as they come so in some ways they don't spoil a pair. Mum can be a bit like that herself. Nextdoor had been there longer than we had, and I can remember them from when I was a kid at home. He used to work at Mason's, where Wayne used to be, well a lot of people round here used to work at Mason's. Nextdoor was in the brass band when Mason's had one, played a cornet or something. They all looked quite smart in their uniforms when they were all dressed up. They even made a record once, for the Coronation or Jubilee or something or other.

All that changed when they were taken over. They said it wouldn't make any difference, but the Yank they put in charge went through them like a dose of salts. When they got rid of the band they said the men could keep their uniforms. I ask you, fat lot of good they were to anyone. Their kids had most of them for dressing up. I saw an old dosser down the precinct wearing one of the caps. I thought, 'That's one of Mason's Works Brass caps'. Then he took it off and spewed up into it. Some of the men had their own instruments, but some belonged to the band. They said they just drove a fork truck up and down over the band's. As they were worth money you'd have thought they'd have flogged them off or even given them away. It upset quite a few of the older ones round here and the union mouthed off, but it didn't make any difference. That's about the time nextdoor retired and took up the pigeons. Bloody things! It's not just the poo, they're so noisy. All the cooing and banging their wings about.

His old woman didn't want the pigeons, for a start. No one got on with her, even when she was younger. Mum says she's gone a bit funny now, never puts her teeth in and slops about in her slippers. Always off down the corner shop. Never buys anything when she gets there. Mum says she smells. When she went out of the shop Mrs Bunjaree just looked at Mum and put the fan on. Mum used to hear them arguing through the wall. 'Get rid of those effing pigeons, or Christ help me I'll effing swing for you.' Well, she never did anything. Old Stoaty never got rid of them. Mum said pity she didn't do him in like she promised, then she'd have got rid of both of them. And the pigeons. But they're still there, making Mum's life a misery. I tell her just to ignore them. I suppose sooner or later the old woman will have to go in somewhere, but that'll still leave the pigeons. Old Stoaty looks as though he'll go on forever.

I suppose there is one thing. When I go to Mum's the boys always run into her back garden and look through the fence to see the birds. Mum says, 'What do you want to go down and look at them things for? Why don't you stay here and talk to your Nana?'. It gives us five minutes peace until they come back and start grizzling to go home. They won't stay still for five minutes. Dad used to keep a tube of Smarties in a drawer for them, and after Dad died Mum did it for a bit, but not now. The house she goes to cleaning, one of the big ones on the New Park estate, the woman there keeps a great bowl of sweets on the side, and Mum takes a good handful before she comes home, but she never had any sweets last time I went. She said when she was there last the woman stared into the bowl and poked them about as much as to say there's not so many in here now as when I looked last time. So Mum thought she'd better give it a rest. Anyway, the both of them are off again on holiday soon, another bloody cruise, so I expect Mum'll have a good poke around when she pops in to see if everything's alright. Mum gets plenty of time there on her own to have a good nosy around.

I never did tell Mum about the old Indian down in Bronte Street. Like I said, I never saw anything, and I wouldn't even have thought about if it hadn't been for the boys calling out. If the twins had been a bit older they might have been winding me up, but not at their age. Though I think the boys are going to be quite clever. Don't know where they get it from. Not me, and certainly not Wayne. No one's seen Wayne or his bit, not that I'd know her anyway – I've never seen her as far as I know. I used to hate her, really hate her. But sometimes I think the poor cow. I admit that Wayne was a smashing-looking guy, and I couldn't believe that Wayne Brandon fancied me, and when we got married I thought I really was the lucky one. They said he used to sleep around a lot, but he told me that I was special, and I believed him. There's one born every minute.

I'm wondering what will happen to number 63. When I went past the other day there was some smooth little guy showing a young Indian couple round, had a baby in a carrycot. They all looked very young, especially the agent git, hardly out of school, but he was wearing a nice new suit. He looked ever so pink. He was quite sweet really. I wondered whether my Red or Wolf might do something like that when they leave school. Well, it's a cut above what Wayne did, or me for that matter. I went from school into the shoe shop, the one down near the town hall in the old part of town. Anyway, it's well gone now. It's that place Ann Summers has just gone into. I'll see when I get down that way. I'm not sure about looking in the window. Someone said it's quite kinky. I won't go inside. They must have gutted the place, as when it was the shoe shop it was that poky. The storeroom was up these awful winding wooden stairs, and we'd go up and down those flaming stairs every five minutes. And no decent loos, just the one we all had to use. Old Ernie Moore used to sit in there for the first hour reading his paper. The girls used to bang on the door busting ourselves, but he wouldn't budge. And the loo paper was that horrible hard stuff. We kept asking for the soft, but they said it was dearer and they couldn't run to it. In the end we brought in our own in our handbags. We wouldn't let Old Moore use it, not that he'd want to. We used to say he was dead from the ass up. Before I had to leave he really did drop dead in there. Well, he didn't *drop* because he was sitting on the throne. When the police broke in they found he hadn't even opened his *Daily Mail*, so he must have popped his clogs as soon as he sat down. They sent us down to the coffee shop when they carried him out.

We were quite serious at first but then we had a good laugh about it, and when we got back it was all neat and tidy and someone had put the air-freshener round. I wished they hadn't, because that was when I came over a bit sicky.

After they opened the new precinct the trade dropped off where we were, and it finished up with just me and another girl, no manager or anything, we just managed ourselves. It was easy-peasy. Anyway, nobody came in the shop much. Then we got this letter from some lawyer to say they were closing down and we'd got the push. So that was that. About that time Janice and me got a letter through the post to say that Old Moore had left us a hundred quid each in his will. Surprise, surprise! The shop never even belonged to him anyway, so why he did that we'll never know. He used to live with his mother and look after her, then she died. Perhaps he fancied us. Ugh! I can't even think about it. Just too gross.

I wasn't married to Wayne then, but we were going out. I wanted to put the hundred quid from Old Moore into the bank for the house when we got it, but Wayne thought we ought to have a day out. So I spent ten pounds on a loo-brush holder from Debenhams, and the rest we blew on a day at Alton Towers. I had to put a bit more towards it, of course. Don't remember a lot about it now. I do know that the loo-brush thing got very stained, and Mum said they were full of germs anyway, so I binned it. Mum was always very good at hygiene. You should see the way she goes through J-cloths! She goes mad over dust and dirt. As well as vacuuming every day, every fortnight she had all the rugs up on the washing line beating the daylights out of them with this old-fashioned beater she picked up at a jumble sale. She always cleaned our windows at home, outside as well as inside, and upstairs. She pushed up the window and sat out on the ledge with her feet hanging down inside. She would lean right back and everyone who saw her thought she was sure to fall out backwards into the street. She had a hook on the wall outside that she used to hang her bucket on. Dad used to say, 'You'll come ass over head out of there one of these days'. Well, she still does it and it hasn't happened yet. And Dad's the one who's gone.

Talking of jumbles, Mum was good at them as well, always outside before they opened up, and straight to what she wanted, elbows going. She went to all the best ones, the Lions, Round Table, Cats Welfare, the Hospice. She knew most of the other women. They'd all like to scratch each others' eyes out. Some of them would buy something and pay with a bigger coin, so that while the bloke was looking away and finding the change they would slide stuff off the table into their bags. They took nice big bags with wide tops. When they were younger I had some lovely stuff for the twins from jumbles, almost new. What people get rid of! Anyway, nowadays everything goes straight to the charity shops and jumbles are a thing of the past.

When I came back today I saw another couple looking over number 63, white, and much older than the other two. An older guy was showing them round, silver hair and tweedy jacket, a bit posh, more New Park estate than Bronte Street,

I thought. No sign of the boy in the suit. I bet those two won't buy it. I can still smell the curry hanging about, though I expect they'd change the curtains. They say places are easier to sell if you leave them up. I'll be quite interested to see who moves in. At least, thinking about it takes my mind off what the boys are doing and passes the time till I get to Dales Road.

After turning into Dales Road it's not far to get to Susie's place where she does the child-minding. There's her own two, a girl and a boy. The girl, Mandy, is a little Downs kid, but she's got a lovely nature. Adam, the boy, is a bit younger, and he's a real little sod. Then there's two other mums bring theirs, Aaron and Jade. They're quite well behaved and don't say much, at least not when I've been there, but Susie says that Aaron can be a bit sly, and can pinch or bite when no one's looking. He'd better not try it on with my Wolf or Red. It's a semi, and round the back there's a shed where we can leave the pushchairs and buggies until we collect the kids to come home. Susie's very easy-going. My boys like her, and she manages to keep them happy, though her size and weight are a bit of a problem. She can just about get through the doors, but quick she is not, and I don't know what she'd do if one of them ran off, because she'd never catch him.

I never see Aaron's mum, but Jade's fancies herself, though why she does I don't know. She doesn't remember me, but she was at my school, and she's no one. She was always in trouble. The mistresses didn't like her, and old Fanny Phillips went raving mad when she saw a condom in her pencil box. I'm surprised that Old Fanny knew what it was. When I told my mum she said that girl's going to end up on the game, you mark my words. She might be on the game now for all I know. They dress quite a bit different when they're off duty. It's mainly car business round here, same as everywhere I suppose.

After dropping the kids I go down to the call centre. I saw the job advertised in the local. There's about seven of us altogether, the girls, a bloke – one old boy and two students, well, they say they're students, but I don't know what they're studying or when they do it. This youngish guy Tony runs it. It could belong to him, as I've never seen any-one else there, except his girlfriend who floats around. She's nicer than Tony, but likes to throw her weight about when he goes out. They both fancy themselves, nice clothes and loads of perfume and aftershave and stuff. We're on the ground floor and his parking space is just under the window. He's always looking out at his car. It's an old silver Merc. He's a slave-driver, only gives us three minutes for the loo, and five minutes for a coffee which we have to buy from this grotty old machine. It's on its last legs and scalded the old chap on the arm the other day. Mind you, he's as cack-handed as they come, and if he can get anything wrong he will. I reckon Tony's going to give him the push.

Tony came up with this idea to phone just people in the area about local businesses, and some of the time he's going round trying to get companies to sign up. So we don't do just double glazing or kitchens, we do all sorts. We've got a couple of butchers, two or three builders, a jewellers, a travel agent, a chiropodist, quite a few different ones. You have to say straight away that you're local and not speaking from India or somewhere. Most of the people you ring up are quite nice after that. One or two give you a mouthful of language, and some of the guys will try chatting you up, quite saucy some of them. Actually, some are dead filthy. I just cut them off and go on to my next number. Someone said that Tony's got another business somewhere where men call up just to hear the girls talking dirty. I couldn't do it, not without a few lessons anyway. Having the lessons would be a bit of a laugh. Hm, that's a thought. What about lessons from Brad Pitt? Then I reckon I might start talking dirty.

Although I don't miss Wayne, or the sex really. I just think sometimes it would be great to have a nice, caring man. I'd exchange Wayne's you-know-what for just a cuddle with a real nice man who loved me and was kind. I never thought I'd hear myself say that, I must be getting old. No, I take it back. I wouldn't mind a bit of something else as well if he was nice. I'm not *that* old, for Christ's sake.

After my shift I go up to Dales Road to collect the twins, and as I turn into Bronte Street it starts to rain. I just have time to pull the waterproof up over the kids and it buckets down. As I get up to number 63 I could see someone had left something on the steps, a pile of clothes or something. Well, it wasn't. Blow me, it was Stoaty Stott's old woman from next door to Mum, just sitting there, looking around without a care in the world, rain hissing down. Her hair was all stuck down over her head and rain all over her glasses. I thought she'll never recognize me.

She looks up, 'Ello,' she says, 'haven't seen you for a long time. How's your mum and dad?'

I thought she was dotty, but apart from forgetting about Dad being gone, I was surprised. I say, 'What you doing down here, Mrs Stott, you're quite a long way from home.'

She says, 'I've been down the shop, but they've moved it again. They're always moving it. And then I lost a slipper.'

And right enough, she's only got one slipper on, and that was all squelchy, like a sponge. Then the boys start acting up, and she says, 'I know what you want. You want to come and look at the pigeons.' I thought I can't stand here in the pouring rain, though I didn't like to leave her there like that, even though she's always been a pain. Just then a car pulls up and it's the boy from the house agent's coming to number 63. He wants to go in but can't get up the steps, so he asks her if she's alright as he guesses there's something wrong or she's not quite all there.

I say, 'She's nothing to do with me, but I do know where she lives.' So I tell him.

He says, 'Oh, I know where that is, we've got a house near there. I'll take her home.' I thought, I hope he knows what he's doing, what with her being wet and goodness knows what else besides. So he puts her in the front seat and goes off, with her all smiles and waving like Royalty. At that minute the rain stops.

I thought that Jade's mum, Katie, would be trouble, 'catty' more like. When we were there picking up the kids yesterday she comes back in and says, 'I left a little rug in Jade's chair and now it's gone. Has anyone seen it?', looking straight at me.

'No,' I say, 'I haven't seen your rug.'

'You sure?' she says.

'Course I am,' I say, 'I wouldn't say so otherwise. I've got plenty of rugs and stuff, I don't need yours.'

'Oh,' she says, 'I'm not accusing no one.'

'No,' I say, 'You'd better not be, neither.'

Then Susie waddles back in. She'd been out to the shed. She holds up a pink rug, not too clean, and says, 'Is this what you're talking about?' Katie grabs it, looks as though she could kill me and Susie and storms off with her kids.

'Thank you, Susie,' I say, all smiles and sweet reason. I didn't want her to think I was like that cow.

Susie drops down in the nearest chair, 'Oh, that's all right,' she says, 'It takes all sorts.'

When I get outside I can hear Susie start singing to her two. She says the little girl likes that. I don't know how she keeps so cheerful. Having her life would crucify me.

Coming back past number 63 there's a van outside and this guy taking down the 'for sale' sign. So without thinking I say, 'Oh, that's been sold then?'

He stops what he's doing and looks at me, 'Coo,' he says, 'you're a real Brain of Britain, you are, why don't you go on for the million?'

I was just going to say something else and the penny

drops that he's taking the piss. Bloody cheek, I was only being friendly. It was the nasty, sneery look he gave me. So I walked on quickly, but I felt my face going red. I was glad he couldn't see it. Some people are so *rude!*

When I get home I was still so mad about it that I popped round Mum's as I wanted to tell her.

'That's men for you,' was all Mum says.

I could tell she had something on her mind. Then she tells me how she ran into old Stoaty's wife coming home in a car with some young guy. Mum said the old girl called out, 'I've just seen your daughter and the boys down in Bronte Street, and then her boyfriend offered me a lift, wasn't that good of him?' Mum gives me a funny look.

I say, 'I thought old mother Stott was supposed to be batty. Seems she's only batty when she wants to be.'

'Don't you worry about her,' Mum says, 'What's all this about a boyfriend of yours down in Bronte Street, with a car? What have you been up to?'

I couldn't believe it. 'I haven't been up to anything. I've only ever seen him once before, and he's *not* my boyfriend! The old woman has made that up.'

Mum looks at me as though she didn't believe me. 'How old is he?' asks Mum.

Then I flare up. 'How should I know? *I don't know him!* He looks about twenty.'

'*Twenty!*' she shrieks, 'that's much too young for you, even if he's got a nice car. At that age he won't know his ass from his elbow. If he gets you up the stick, my girl, don't come running to me for help. You've got the twins already.

And you should never have had them. You ought to have more sense. If you *must* have it, why don't you just get one of those horrible things they sell in your old shop, but for God's sake don't get involved with another man! If you do, I tell you, Mary, I've finished with you. I really mean that.'

Well, I just walked out. I could not believe it. Even my own mother doesn't know me. Surely she knows I just wouldn't *do* that. I've *never* been like that. To hear her talk you'd think that I'd pick up with any guy who came along. I just don't believe it. She is something else, just something else. I'm sorry I went round there now. A bit of sarcy lip from a guy taking down a board I can put up with, but when your own mother can get it so wrong! I feel as though she's just kicked me in the face.

I just couldn't sleep, with the day I'd had. What Mum had said just kept going round and round in my head and I kept thinking how wrong she was about me. After all these years she doesn't really know me. And Red and Wolf kept waking up and saying they were hot and asking for a drink. I'd just got them off and was dropping off myself and there was a great racket from outside, shouting and laughing and banging about with people coming out of 'The Queens'. Someone started kicking over the empty milk bottles, where they still have a milkman. Then the window went at the shop down on the corner. I thought why don't they just bloody well go home? I just drew the covers up and had a good cry, I felt that rotten and completely pissed off with everything and everybody. I can understand why people top themselves.

Next morning I felt as though I hadn't been to sleep, but I guess I had. But I still felt rotten. By the time I went out with the kids someone was putting plywood over the window of the shop, and a neighbour had kicked the bits of milk bottle into the gutter. I don't know how long they'll stay there, as we only get that big sweeper through once in a blue moon, and half the time it misses the gutters because of the parked cars.

While I'm handing the boys over to Susie and telling them to be good, that Katie walks in. She looks deadly white, and some of her hair at the front had been razored off where she'd had a cut in her head with three big black stitches across it. Looked like an A & E job. She had a bit of a black eye on the same side.

Susie says, 'Oh dear, Katie, you been in the wars?'

'Yea,' says Katie, 'silly me, I left one of the doors open on the kitchen unit and walked straight into it.'

'Oh dear,' says Susie. I said nothing, as I hadn't forgiven her for all that fuss about the rug. I didn't believe her story anyway, and I don't expect Susie did either. My guess is that her old man had a go at her, or maybe, if she really is tomming it, then one of her clients got a bit stroppy. Anyway, she buzzes off pretty quick after plonking Jade down and sticking Tigger in her hand.

So I go off down to the call centre. The Mazda is in Tony's space, and sure enough there's Blondie – her real name's Jackie – sitting at Tony's desk. The old man hasn't turned up and one of the girls has phoned in sick. They find out that last night Tony had locked up all our headsets and gone off with the keys in his pocket, so no one can get plugged in. So we just sit around talking or reading the papers and stuff, while Jackie gets more and more aerated trying to track down Tony on his mobile. She gets him and tells him about the keys, and he says they're in the middle drawer of his desk, and it's not locked. So I hear him sounding off and calling her a stupid c-word for not looking there. And she keeps asking him 'where are you?', but I don't think he ever said where he was. I could see from the look on her face that she thought he wasn't at home and he'd just got out of bed, and it wasn't his bed and it sure wasn't hers. So as soon as we get the headsets plugged in she says, 'I'm just popping out, I won't be long'. And she gets into the Mazda and shoots off. They say Tony's got a flat in the Old Mill conversion down by the river, and I bet that's where she was off to. At least she'd put out all the call sheets, so we knew who to phone. Tony keeps promising us a new system where you don't need sheets, it's all in the computer, but it hasn't come yet.

Around half-ten we gang up on one of the boys, the one we call The Weakling, and make him go and get the coffee for us. He's only gone a few minutes, and he comes back in with the tea towel wrapped round his arm, scalded in exactly the same place as the old man was. He's making a real fuss, nearly in tears. So they all flock round him and persuade him to unwind the tea towel so we can take a look, but there's hardly a mark on him, his arm just a bit pink. So we all tease him, and he goes off and makes the coffee and doesn't mention his arm again.

Then Blondie comes back looking pretty mad. We just carry on with our calls as normal. Then Tony breezes up. I saw him turn to go into his space and find her Mazda there. He walks in and glares at Blondie and points out of the window and says, 'Move it'.

'Can't you park somewhere else?' she says. He doesn't answer, just repeats, 'Move it'. She could have killed him, but goes out with a face like thunder. A minute later there's a bang and breaking glass and some of us look out of the window. Blondie has only reversed out of Tony's space and caught the back end of an empty school bus going by. Tony, Blondie and the bus driver stand out there arguing the toss, and then a police car going by sees them at it and stops and a couple of bobbies get out and join in. Most of us just roll about laughing, and even the boy with the arm enjoys it. One of the bobbies starts walking round Blondie's Mazda, then gets into it with her. Then the bus drives off. The Mazda's back end looks a bit chewed up, but the Law gets out and Blondie tears off down the street. Tony puts his Merc into his space and comes back into the office. Does he look mad or does he look mad? By this time we are all back on the job and dialling away and talking to our numbers.

I have the usual calls, and am just talking to a woman down on the industrial estate over by the railway and she says her boss can't come to the phone because he's been called away as some guy has just been fried down a manhole. I ask her what she's talking about and she says, 'Well, love, that's what happens to you if you get a few thousand volts shot up your ass. He came straight up out of the manhole as though he'd been shot out of a canon.'

'Oh,' I say, 'that sounds like bad news. Is he dead?'

'I should say, love,' she says, 'he's like a bloody great pig what's been roasted on a spit, barbecue style. Every scrap of clothes blasted off him.' Then she whispered, 'someone who moved him said that even his dick was well fried. And there's still a black patch on the concrete where he landed.'

I say I'd ring back another time, but ask her, 'what was this guy doing down in the manhole anyway?' and she says, 'When he got the job he made out he was a sparks, and he went down to investigate the HT cable, but we reckon he was telling porkies and he was no more an electrician than my Aunt Fanny. My boss is livid about it. He'd have his guts for garters if he wasn't brown bread.'

It took me a few minutes to get it out of my head, the thought of this guy shooting up out of the manhole like a burnt pig. I'm glad I wasn't there, it would have turned me up. At least the poor bugger wouldn't have known much about it. I'd just started on my next call and there's a great clatter and I look up to see the boy who'd scalded his arm falling on the floor and, still wired-up, pulling a lot of gear off his work-top as he goes down. He's kicking about and moving his head around and making a funny noise, and we all stand round wondering what to do. Tony comes up, 'Now what?' he says. He stands there looking at him and says, 'He's having a fit or something. Leave him where he is, and if he's no better in ten minutes one of you best get the ambulance. Rest of you go and sit down and get on with it.'

Well, we couldn't concentrate with him wriggling about

on the floor and moaning.

One of the girls says, 'I think we ought to call 999.'

Tony starts to lose his rag and says, 'You do as I bloody say and get on with your work. I'm not paying you to chase around after this snotty-nosed little shit.'

After a bit the boy stops jigging about and opens his eyes and gets up and sits back in his chair. I look at him and make the words 'Are you OK?' without saying anything. He just nods and puts his headset back on and sorts out his work-top. He still looks white and his hands shake a bit. I guess he's epileptic and that he'd had a fit or something, like Tony said. When I'd finished I go and get my coat, and I hear Tony call the boy over to his desk, but I had to get off before I could hear any more.

I was a bit late getting to Susie's and Jade and Aaron were already gone. Susie says, 'You won't be seeing Katie again, because Jade won't be coming any more. There's been some sort of fuss with Jade's dad, and Katie is going to live with one of Jade's uncles. Jade is staying with her dad for now until they can sort it, but he won't be bringing her here any more.' I thought good riddance, though Jade was quite a nice little kid. Perhaps she took after her dad and not that cow of a Katie.

That evening I'd just got the kids up to bed and was settling down for a bit of telly and there's the doorbell. When I see two coppers I nearly jump out of my skin, then I think, 'I know, it's Blondie and the bus, they're looking for witnesses.'

The woman says, 'Mrs Brandon?', and the bobby takes

his cap off, and I say, 'That's me.'

She says, 'May we come in?' So I let them in, and the other one says he thinks I ought to sit down. That worries me a bit, then he says, 'Is your husband Wayne Brandon?' And I nod, and then he tells me there's been an accident and that Wayne's dead. I couldn't take it in, but I do say that he walked out on me and I hadn't seen him for ages. Then they say it was an accident at work and he was electrocuted, at this factory on the industrial estate down by the railway yard. Of course, I put two and two together and nearly pass out. To think that was Wayne down the manhole and being... like the woman told me this morning. It was just too horrible. I start crying and then thought I would throw up.

The policewoman holds my hand and says to the copper, 'Go through to the kitchen and fix the lady a cup of tea, Jack.'

So he goes off and I hear him filling the kettle, and she just sits there while I keep trying to sort my thoughts out. The copper comes back with the tea in a dirty old beaker I haven't used for ages. I don't know where he found it. I've got several nice ones. I can't honestly say that Wayne meant a lot to me at that moment, because he'd killed what we had when he walked out on me for that woman from Mason's. At first I suppose I had hoped he might come back again, but as time went on I missed him less and less, and although my job and my allowances never came to as much as the money I got from Wayne, I did manage to get by. I don't think I'll say anything to the boys just now. They seem to have forgotten about him, and I won't remind them. I can tell them when they're older. And I'll tell Mum, she'll have to know, but she went on so much about this so-called boyfriend of mine that I won't tell her too much. And when I said to the police about Wayne going off. I think, in a way, they were quite relieved, as I expect they thought I would throw a wobbly when they told me he's dead. I think I was pretty good really. But Wayne popping up out of the manhole all black and burnt, that really got to me, and it will haunt me, I know it will.

Well, I never dreamt about Wayne, slept real fine, in fact. I guess I was tired. I thought I'd better tell Mum what had happened, so when I get up I ring her. I could tell straight off that something was up.

I just say, 'Mum, Wayne was killed at work yesterday.'

All she says was, 'Good job, he was never no good to you. Now listen to this. Next door are going and taking the flamin pigeons. They're both moving into a council flat with a warden to keep an eye on the old woman, and a friend of Stoaty's is having the pigeons. I can't believe it, after all these years I'm getting shot of them. No more aggro from any of them, and my washing's going to be real clean again.'

I say, 'That's great news.'

'I'm real happy,' Mum says, 'now I've got to go as I'm just going to scrub the kitchen floor.' And she was gone.

Then it hit me. I was still like married to Wayne, and now there would be things to do, official things, like signing papers and stuff. And the funeral. Someone would be coming round about that. How was I going to pay for it?

Who else would pay, for God's sake? Not that tart of his, that's for sure. Won't see her ass for dust now her meal ticket's gone. So I just sit on the stairs and cry my eyes out. The kids see me, and that starts them off bawling the place down. Then someone starts knocking on the front door. I think, 'they didn't take long. Which one of them is it, the police, the Social, the undertaker?' I felt like buzzing off out the back door, just leaving the kids and getting away, didn't matter where, just anywhere.

Anyway, after a bit I open the door. I guess she was from the Social, middle-aged, with a red anorak and a big hand-bag. The kids stop crying. They get curious when someone fresh comes to the door.

'Mrs Brandon?' she says. I think 'here we go again, I'm not sure how much of this I can take.' So I nod, and she asks to come in. I was about all-in so I just point to a chair, and sit down myself. The woman looks white and worked up, as though she hadn't done this before, which I thought was a bit unlikely.

'I'm not sure where to start,' she says. 'I worked at Mason's, and I knew your Wayne.'

'Oh yeah,' I say, 'well he's been long gone from there, because that's where his fancy woman worked, and they both left there when he walked out on me. You must know that anyway.'

The woman was getting right wound up now, and just nods. Then she says, starting to cry, 'I was the woman. Wayne left you for me.'

I just stare at her. What I was hearing didn't go with what

I was seeing. My eyes nearly pop out of my head.

'Wayne walked out on me for a right old boiler like you? I don't believe it. You, a fat old has-been, old enough to be his fuckin' mother! Sorry, I don't buy it. I just don't believe any of this. It's a bloody wind-up. Bugger off, I've got enough problems without some joker like you turning up and spinning me a tale.'

'No,' she says, 'it's true. I wish it weren't, but it is true.'

I just looked at her. I couldn't get my head round it, no way. Then some of it starts to come back to me.

'Then who was the woman people saw with Wayne down the precinct, and what about the kid they saw him pushing around in the chair? Don't tell me that was you, and your brat.'

At that she starts sobbing, and her handbag falls on the floor and all the stuff comes out. She leaves it all there, and so did I. I thought, sod it.

She doesn't speak for a bit, then she comes out with, 'The woman is my Donna, and the kid in the pushchair is her Darren. After he left Mason's Wayne was bored out of his skull, and used to run my Donna into the centre, and take the boy out just to pass the time. He couldn't get another job.'

Then I think, 'hold on'. So I say, 'You said you worked at Mason's. I thought Wayne and his woman both chucked their jobs in?'

She looks at me and shakes her head. 'Believe me, I didn't want Wayne to leave you, or to chuck his job. I never chucked mine, I'm just now retired, from Accounts. I was amazed when Wayne turned up at my place with all his gear and said he was moving in. I didn't want that. In fact, I didn't want him, full stop. I wouldn't let him in, but somehow he'd got it into his head that we had a future together. He'd got it all wrong. So he went off. I must have been mad to do what I did. They said that at one time or another he'd had most of the younger ones who'd let him, and I guess I was flattered that he'd look at me. Everyone thought he was that good looking. Anyway, I had been married. He was in the Army, and I lost him in a silly accident on the ranges while they were training on Salisbury Plain. I feel so ashamed – my Bob was worth twenty of Wayne and I always knew it. Anyway, Wayne kept coming back, wanting me to let him stay, but after that one and only time at Mason's I wouldn't let him touch me. I felt so ashamed. He just wouldn't take no for an answer and he thought that if he moved in with me it would all be different. I told him to go back to you, kept on telling him, but he took no notice. That's when he should have come back to you, but he wouldn't so he went into a room and then a caravan. Someone said he'd picked up with a schoolgirl and got her in the family way, but I don't know for sure.'

'Yeah,' I said, 'that sounds like Wayne! Anyway, I wouldn't have had him back. It's been hard work, but after the first shock I didn't really miss him. Anyway, he's dead now.'

She starts crying again and pokes about on the floor for a hanky.

'What's your name?'

She sniffs a bit, 'Dorothy, but they call me Dot.'

We sit there looking at each other and I almost start to feel sorry for the silly old bat.

'What's your daughter think about all this?'

'Upset. She was mad at me for being so stupid. She never really liked Wayne, though she let him push Darren round in his chair once or twice. She was glad when he left me alone and disappeared.'

I say, 'I didn't want to know any of this. I don't know why you've come anyway. It's been bad enough for me, without your hard luck story and crying around. You knew bloody well what you were doing. Christ knows, you're certainly old enough.'

'I know, I know,' she says. 'I've felt so ashamed about it all, that I needed to speak to you and try to make up for it in some way. Look here, will you let me pay for Wayne's funeral, or something. I've just retired from Mason's so I've got a little bit of money. You must have found things pretty hard.'

It's on the tip of my tongue to say, 'Well, you don't see a bloody Roller parked outside, do you?' and I hear myself saying, 'OK. I'll let you pay for the funeral.'

At that she seems real pleased. But by that time she'd been there long enough for the kids to get used to her and start playing up, showing off and doing that silly giggling all the time, so in next to no time she ups and goes, saying she'll come back.

I slept well again that night. I think I'd always really knew that Wayne had been having it off with the Masons women, though I'd always preferred not the think about it. But to be told that he'd left me for that Dot woman, well, I just couldn't believe it. I'd always thought he'd gone with some tarty bit of a girl, one of those on the line, but to find he'd actually left me for an old bag from the office with one foot in the grave. Well, for one thing it was a bloody insult to me, and whether he's dead or not I can never forgive him for that. Leaving me for that! What in God's name does that make me look like? Still, that aside, she seems OK, and in some ways easier to talk to than my own mum is these days. I never knew Wayne's mum, but he always said she was crap, so perhaps that's why he took to this old biddy. It's all a bit creepy if you ask me.

Anyway, I get the kids up and get off down to Susie's with them. When I get there there's a battered old Escort outside and an old man opens the door, with a fag in his mouth.

'Have you brought some kids?' he says. 'Well, you can't leave them. My niece's had a stroke, and I'm waiting for the ambulance to come.' And I look inside and there's Susie sitting back in her chair just staring straight ahead and not talking. She looked like she was still in her night things. I didn't know what to do, so I just call through the door, 'Hope you'll be better soon, Susie' but she never hears me and just looks straight in front of her, and the old man can't shut the door on me quick enough.

Once I was on the pavement I just stand there. There was no way I could take the boys down to the call centre with me, as Tony would kill me on the spot and then give me my cards. There was nothing to do but ring Mum to see if she'd take them off my hands. So I ring her on my mobile. No answer. I got her a mobile for emergencies but she never takes it out with her, so no reply there either. So I'd have to phone Tony to say I'd be late or take a sickie, or something. Either way I'd lose the money. So I start phoning Tony and find I'm nearly outside the old Indian's place in Bronte Street, with two women with a buggy and a kid in it just coming out. They slam the door behind them, and blow me one of them is that Dot woman who came round yesterday. She sees me and calls out, quite friendly. It turns out that the other woman is her daughter who has actually bought the house because she and her man want to move out of their flat. And she ends up with a place that I've been walking past every day! Now is that or is that not creepy? It's all bloody creepy if you ask me.

'I've told my Donna about what happened yesterday,' says this Dot woman. 'You just on your way to work?'

So as I'm a bit full up, I tell her about the job and how Susie has had a stroke and I'm just ringing the office.

'Oh,' says Donna, 'We've found the mobile reception pretty grotty round here so come in and use the landline.' So they go back in and I follow them in with my two. I will say, she really has got it nice. The front room is bigger than I'd thought, with a lovely dark red carpet and a white leather suite, and she's changed the curtains. Her Darren and my two kids start talking in their own way, and we all sit down and she hands me the phone. That's when I get another surprise, because when I ring I find that the office is on answer machine, like it is at week-ends. I've never known that before, there's always someone to answer the phone, either Tony or Blondie, or even one of us if they're both out.

'It says the office is closed, but I can't believe it. I'll have to go down there to find out.'

Then Donna says, 'Why don't you leave your boys here while you go? It'll be quicker, and they're quite happy playing with Darren. There's a load of toys and stuff in the other room, so they'll be OK.'

I wasn't too sure about it, but Donna and her mum seemed really pleased, so I decided to go down to the office to check it out. The boys saw me go, but they were so busy with Darren that they took no notice at all.

When I get down there, true enough, the place is all shut up with no car outside. Then The Weakling comes round the corner looking as puzzled as I was. He says he's been to the doctor's and just arrived for work and found the place locked up. We'd just decided to pack it in and go, when I spot a Post-it note on the ground.

'Looks as though it's come unstuck,' he says. Anyway, all it said was CLOSED. We stand there looking at each other for a bit, then he goes off on his bike, and I go back to No 63 to pick up the kids.

They'd been having a great time – hadn't missed me at all. Darren's toys were all over the floor, and Donna and her mum are having a brew and say would I like one. They're real nice to me. But I say I can't stop, as I was upset about the job and wanted to sort it out, although I didn't know where to start.

Anyway, they persuade me to have a cup, and say why don't I ring once more from here in case someone's turned up at the office. So I do that, and it rings a bit, and I was just going to give it up and someone answers.

'Hallo,' says this woman, 'it's Jacqueline here.'

'Who?' I say.

'Jacqueline, Jackie, at the call centre. There's been some trouble, Mary.'

I say, 'You're telling me. I've been to work today and the place is all shut.'

'I know,' she says. 'The problem is... Tony's been up to something and the police have taken him in. I don't know what it's about, you must believe me. But it seems the bank has stepped in and grabbed everything, and they want to speak to me. They say they would like to keep the centre going and want like me to run it at least until it's all sorted.'

'Well, there's my job gone down the Swanny,' I say.

'No,' she says, 'well, it might be, it all depends on whether the bank can sort out the money side. I don't mind having a go at running the centre and stuff, but I'm trying to get hold of people to see if they'll carry on without Tony.'

'Only too glad to, I'd say. You must admit, Jackie, he's been a right bastard to everyone.'

'I know,' says Jackie, real choked. 'Don't tell me. You don't know the half of it. We had something going once, but I've found out the hard way he doesn't care a toss about anyone else except himself. He takes, takes, takes all the time, gives nothing back. I wish I'd never set eyes on him.

He's a right wanker. Anyway, I'm here at the office now, with a guy from the bank going through a few things. He seems quite hopeful that it can all get sorted and we can carry on the business ourselves. We might even be in line for a grant for starting up a new business – well, it would be new without Tony, wouldn't it? Will you come down tomorrow and help me out? I'd be ever so grateful. I'm asking you because you know the job and are better at it than any of the others.'

'Well,' I say, 'I'd like to, but I've nowhere to leave the kids now, as the woman who looks after them has had a stroke.'

Then Donna starts waving her arms. 'Why don't you leave your boys with me? My firm lets me work at home with the computer so I can keep an eye on my Darren, and another couple of kids won't make any difference.'

So I ring off and say I'll call Jackie back.

'It's a really great offer, Donna, but my two can be a real handful. Though they do seem to get along with your Darren OK.'

Donna is now quite excited, and her mum says that she's often there at No. 63 now she's retired so she could lend a hand, and having Red and Wolf really wouldn't be a problem. In fact, it would give her something to do.

Anyway, I go home and get a bit of tea and put the boys to bed when the phone rings. It's the guy from the Uni who brought round the recorder and all these sticks or tapes or whatever they are, Bill someone. I'm surprised how much I've done. He says he now wants to collect it all and have a listen to it. And he's also bringing my cheque for £250, which was what he agreed for me taking part in his Social Record thing. He says it's supposed to give a snapshot of different people's lives in this particular place and at this particular time. If it's ever published, he says the names will be changed. I certainly hope so.

Perhaps I've been too personal in what I've said. Anyway, I hope that what I've done is what he wants. In spite of what I thought, Donna's old mum seems OK, and will help out with the boys. It's really funny how the boys will be going to No 63 instead of Susie's, and how we used to walk by that house and wave to the old Indian man. He always looked friendly, so I hope that's a good omen.

I'm glad that Tony's gone from the call centre. He was a pretty horrible guy. And I hope that Jackie can keep it going and we shall still have jobs. I might find out a bit more tomorrow. If she can convince the bank that we're up to it and that they won't lose their money, then we might have a chance. Otherwise, we're all up shit creek.

Now I really must stop chattering into this thing. Bill from the Uni is due here at seven tomorrow to pick his gear up. He says if his project is a success and he can get some more money out of someone he might come back in a few years and do it all again. He says he will want to know what Wolf and Red are doing when they get older. Christ knows where we shall be by that time. Still, I said I'd do it again if I'm still around. The money would still be handy. Anyway, I'm hoping for an early night. So I'm turning this thing off.

Poems

Alice and Edith
According to Betjeman?

'Passing the Peace' –
What *can* I say?
My sister, Edith, *loves* it,
Shaking hands, in and out of pews,
She dashes round, and comes back
To my side quite out of breath.

The young man next to me
Is *very* nice.
He wears a stripy jumper,
And looks so *tough*,
But, oh, he smells *divine*.

The people in the chancel make more fuss,
'The kiss of peace', they say,
And *kiss* they do,
Right on the *lips*, like Mum and Dad
Did all those years ago.

It's nice to see them,
But, at the end,
The Rector always wipes his lips.
His hanky always looks so neat,
All folded, white,
Thanks to his sister, Jo.
She works *so* hard
To keep the Rector looking *nice*.

Blackout

May 2001

My life-support's switched off,
By I live on.
The x-rays, scans and all,
They show no change,
Except I know the damage is severe
And can't be healed.

So often, so they say,
Internal bleeding causes death,
Yet on the body not a mark
To give the game away.

You see, we had been wired together
For so long
That when the circuit-breaker tripped
There's half my systems gone –
No, more than half.

Yet still the lights are on,
And no external marks to see,
And give the game away.

Breakfast TV

The sofa warped beneath his weight,
His beer-gut spread between his knees,
A giant cantaloupe
Fit to be wheeled to village hall
To claim first prize.

A man behind the scenes
Gave him his cue –
'How did you feel?'
The fat man moved,
The belly bulged,
His belt now lost to sight
In darkest pubic folds.

The nation waited,
But at last he spoke:
'Well, I wuz gah-idd,
Wan I?'

The kipper on my plate
With two-eyed stare
Looked up, and cried,
'That man's a bloody liar,
Inny?'

Voice from Lethe

I can't remember where I was
When the bit broke off the sun;
I can't remember where I was
When the continents begun.

I can't remember what I did
When fish turned into birds;
I can't remember what I did
When Noah saved his herds.

I can't remember what I said
When Pilate washed his hands;
I can't remember what I said
When Hitler schemed and planned.

I can't remember what I thought
When New York's towers fell down;
I can't remember what I thought
When the Windsors lost the crown.

I can't remember how I felt
When all the world was drowned;
I can't remember how I felt
When no living thing was found.

Just as I was
So am I now –
It's all the same to me –
All memory is elided
Throughout eternity.

Crossing Point

This is an open border –
No let or hindrance here
For anyone.
Steadily the queue moves forward,
No searches, visas, declarations,
You just step over this,
See here, this line drawn in the sand.

When people reach the line
Some hesitate, the older ones,
The young ones don't think twice,
There, they're over it,
Without once looking down.

They used to call this line
A bourne, a word now out of use.
We thought the sandy line
More fitting for these days.
It's really all the same,
Once there, they stay.
From that side of the line
No emigration is allowed.
To tell the truth, enforcement there
Is the envy of the world.

Face to Face

My eyesight's now quite good,
But what I want to see I can't –
I can't see Heaven,
For you or me or anyone.

Maybe my wavelength's wrong,
Or Evolution has too far to run
To share that secret now
With animals like us.

The attributes of time and place
And all they mean to me
Will not condense or render down
To just one instant of eternity.

Maybe, encoded on some microchip,
It's there,
The Word beyond our view.
It bides its time,
Till Omega shall smash Paul's darkened glass.

Family Man

He's next in line for Cabinet,
They say.
See how his eyes traverse the room,
See how he smiles
And looks like one of us.
He binds us by the eyeball
To himself.
He's next in line for Cabinet,
They say.

And yet that mouth, not quite the same.
No, something of the mouth is wrong.
That's where the charm offensive peters out.
When woolly mikes and torrid lights have gone
Could that same mouth frame 'fucking cow'
And more, behind that door?

And could those feet, on leave from mountains green,
Kick out at 'her' and loveless kids.
And does he cheat on both,
And when, at last grown tired of pieties,
Does he refresh himself with easy girls and boys?

Does guileful, bullying teenager rule here,
Behind that door?
No, surely not,
He's next in line for Cabinet, they say.
What's more, the Ministry of Culture's up for grabs.

Genesis Updated

'Is he winding me up?' asked Adam.
'Yes, he's taking the piss,' said Eve.
'He's chucked us out of the Garden,
And he's only given us leaves.'

'I tell you, I'm flamin' livid,
Who put the serpent there?
And who created the apple?
That silly old git upstairs!'

Said Adam, 'I'm well gutted,
I think we've got a case,
Big damages are called for,
With Human Rights the basis.'

'There's no case law for this,' said God,
'You're the first of human kind,
I'm a victim of my own success,
Please bear this in your mind.'

'Not good enough,' said Adam,
'My partner's been distressed,
Suppose she can't have children,
Or her sex life's in a mess?
'She's already getting flashbacks
And she's gone right off her food,

Said God, 'I won't say sorry,
But lessons have been learned,
I'll pay your costs and damages,
But I do have other concerns.'

'I can't help that,' said Adam,
'It's devastated Eve,
We were absolutely gobsmacked
When you told us both to leave!'

'All right,' said God, 'All right, *all right*!
Spare me the tongue pie, do.
I thought you were my children,
But the snake turned out better than you.'

Just 'John'

My tears still flow.
Bring shining litre flasks
To measure them.
Make sure no drop is missed
So I may qualify.
'For what?', you ask.
There's nothing else I want
Except to hear her voice just once.
'And saying what?', you ask.
That's easy. Just my name,
Just 'John' in her own voice.

How many tears I shed
They're not enough to qualify
And work that miracle,
To hear that name again.

Except, just maybe, at my end
God's angel, Morphia, will make it so,
And I shall hear her say that word –
Just, 'John',
Before the end.

'Oh Shit!'

I wish I was cool and awfully laid back
And had learnt to say 'shit!' at the drop of a hat,
But the hat doesn't drop,
And if the vin rouge should slop,
I never cry 'shit!' but 'bugger that!'

But 'shit!' is so classy,
Kinda Stateside and sassy,
How I wish it would roll off my tongue.
Though I would it were other
My default mode is 'bugger!',
A word rarely used by the young.

It's no use my raging,
But 'bugger!' is ageing,
It's uncool and horribly naff.
Now that 'shit!' is the fashion
My 'buggers!' I'll ration,
And try hard not to make such a gaffe.

Party Time?

Golden lads and girls all must,
As chimney-sweepers, come to dust.

Cymbeline, Act iv, scene 2

Is this a party game?
The lights go out,
With finger to his lips
The host bids, 'Hush'.

Some golden lads and girls
Have gone to play the game,
But some delayed
Until the gold was dull and grey.

Do they enjoy the game?
They play it well
And make no sound at all.
Their host is pleased, I hope.

My invite hasn't come,
Though it is promised,
And when it does,
And I set off in party clothes,
The chimney-sweeper says
    He'll take my arm
And walk with me.

Worsted

The tailor flicked the heavy bolt of cloth
With practised hand
Across the cutting table,
An oblong wheel,
Unwinding, softly thudding,
Comforting.

Here was pleasure to be had,
Soft worsted, caressed with open hand,
Smoothed, inviting admiration,
And on the air the faintest tang
Of weaving shed and landscape
Far north or west of here.

The tailor turned his eyes on me,
A look that's found where rooms are locked,
And medication never missed.
'This cloth, sir, is Eternity,
With no beginning and no end,
And somewhere in the middle
A single thread of gold is woven in,
That golden strand is...
What would you say, sir,
Is it life or death?
I want to know.'

I took my hand away,
As though the cloth had been
His workroom iron, left on too long.
The tailor and his bolt of cloth
Both watched me go.
Suddenly I saw a vision
Growing in my mind
Of rows of ready-made in M and S...
I knew I should have gone there first.

Scripts for Sketches

1 A Prime Minister Speaks

The Prime Minister is to be interviewed for television.

INT. *A drawing room in No. 10 Downing Street. Marble fireplace. On one side seated the Prime Minister, Ben Baskett, on the other his interviewer, Julian Stoke-Poges. Both occasionally sip glasses of a colourless liquid, Ben Baskett openly, Julian surreptitiously when he thinks he's out of shot.*

JULIAN

Good morning, Prime Minister.

BEN

Nice to meet with you again Julian.

JULIAN

Prime Minister, we're here at No. 10 today at your request to dispel, as you put it, the wild rumours that have been sweeping the world's media closely concerning you, as a man, and your lifestyle

BEN

That's right, Julian. I've always known this would come to light, of course, but recent DNA tests have put it beyond doubt. There are also, ...er... physical signs.

JULIAN

It must have taken great courage on your part, and I
know that the world will respect you for it.

BEN

(clearly under some emotion)

Thank you Julian, it's not been easy for any of us, especially my dear wife and our children.

JULIAN

I know this may be embarrassing to you and come as
a shock to viewers, but would you like to tell us the secret that you have been keeping over the years?

BEN

Yes, Julian.

(swallows hard and pauses)

JULIAN

Take your time, Prime Minister.

BEN

The fact is – I have genes of the Black Rat in my blood,
proper name, rattus rattus. Not to be confused with
rattus norvegicus, which is the brown rat, a much
newer strain, as the name implies, from Norway.

JULIAN

I didn't think that was possible.

BEN

Oh yes. It's very easy to confuse the brown rat and the black rat.

JULIAN

No, Prime Minister, I meant I didn't think it was possible for a human being to acquire the genes of any rat species, except, maybe, by injection.

BEN

Well, Julian, there is an obvious way.

JULIAN

You can't mean by...by some form of... sexual congress?

BEN

Exactly so. It was all a long time ago, and don't forget 'there are more things in heaven and on earth than...' etc., etc.

JULIAN

That's true. Can you tell us a little more?

BEN

Well, Julian, as you may know I come from a very old Norfolk farming family who have lived on the land for centuries. We reckon it was about three centuries ago that one of the Baskett girls had a little too much to drink and while sleeping it off in one of the haybarns was 'taken advantage of' by a particularly bold specimen of rattus rattus.

JULIAN

That's far from a happy thought, Prime Minister.

BEN

Indeed not. But, I can assure you, in those parts not an entirely unique event.

JULIAN

How utterly frightful. So what happened?

BEN

Well, fortunately the Norfolk Baskett genes have proved somewhat stronger than the rattus rattus genes, and few of the more obvious rattus features have persisited in my family. But – they are still there.

JULIAN

Which features in particular?

BEN

Well, Julian, the men and women in the family are differently blessed. The women are born with strong black movable whiskers either side of the upper lip – what's known in the family as 'the Baskett brush' These whiskers are twitchable..

JULIAN
That must have been embarrassing for them?

BEN
Well, they coped, they coped. After the girls reached puberty the head gardener would come up to the house every week with something suitable from his toolshed, just to trim the ends of the whiskers. Nowadays all the girls just get a top-of-the-range Braun or Philips trimmer on their eighteenth birthday. And modern make-up does wonders for the after-brush.

JULIAN
I see. So what did the men of the family inherit?

BEN
Well, this is really how the matter became public knowledge, after my old-fashioned London tailor died. Dear old boy. Absolutely discreet.

JULIAN
So what happened?

BEN
Well, the awful fellow who bought the business straight away went around blabbing about peoples' measurements. Some of them were very surprising indeed! I couldn't believe what he told me about one member of the Board of Admiralty! It was unforgiv-

able of him, of course. Anyway, next thing the gossip was all over London.

JULIAN
What was all over London, Prime Minister?

BEN
Wake, up, Julian. My leg measurement, of course, my leg measurement. One narrow leg, one wide leg.

JULIAN
Well? I'm not sure how that is significant.

Ben tuts with frustration at Julian's dimness.

BEN
The wide leg is where I normally keep my tail, of course!

Ben eases up from his chair, puts his hand under his rump and brings his rat's tail round from under him and lays it across his knees. Julian is speechless. Eventually he stammers out:

JULIAN
That is…is…incredible!

BEN
Well, it may be to you, but, I assure you, not to the Basketts of Norfolk. The Baskett men all have tails as

well as heads.

JULIAN
So why isn't your tail down your trouser leg, as usual?

BEN
Well, Julian, after word got out on some of the red tops, we found that certain young party activists, mainly women, were sewing fabric tails on to their jeans. So it just seemed that the time had come for the Basketts to 'come out', as it were.

JULIAN
So that's why some of the girls at the clubs have tails! And I thought it was all to do with a promotion for the show Cats!

BEN
No, I think it's all down to me. Actually, some of the tails look quite fetching, with graduated sequins, very tiny ones towards the tip of the tail, of course.

JULIAN
I take it that you have never decorated your own tail in any way?

BEN
No, but I did do something rather special with it on our honeymoon, but I think that will have to stay very

firmly between Tabitha and me, don't you?

JULIAN

Of course, of course. So what happens now?

BEN

Well, I'm pleased to say that I've found another tailor, and he's in the course of making a large button-hole in the seat of all my pairs of trousers. We're callng it my 'tail-gate'. I'm leaving the legs as they are.

JULIAN

Well, I do congratulate you on coping so wonderfully with such an unusual issue, Prime Minister.

BEN

Thank you. I've had great support from my family, of course. My youngest daughter Deborah, who's at fashion school, is even now designing me a range of attractive tail-sleeves for all occasions.

JULIAN

I'm sure she'll do it beautifully. Now, viewers, I'm afraid we have to end it there. Thank you, Prime Minister. It's been a privilege talking to you.

BEN

Not at all. It's been a pleasure talking to you, Julian.

Both men stand up. Ben throws his tail over his left arm like carrying a raincoat, and shakes hands. Both men stand still for a few seconds, and a technician with headphones comes into shot. Everyone thinks they are off air, but they are not.

JULIAN

Thank you, Prime Minister. I think that went very well. You show there's always a silver lining.

BEN

A silver lining? Yes, a tail sleeve with a silver lining? Good suggestion, Julian. I'll pass that idea on to Deborah. (about here, the sound starts fading out) Shame it's such a limited market otherwise she could do very well with...

SLOW VISION FADE

END

2 Anglo-Saxon Spinners

About 1064 AD, a couple of years before the Norman Conquest. Edward the Confessor is king.

INT. A sparsely furnished, dimly lit room in a castle in Southern England. Gurth is sitting at a table, Norfryth returns to the room. Both have been drinking wine from goblets, which they intermittently top up from a large flagon. The effects of this become more pronounced as the scene progresses. Gurth is a bit camp.

GURTH

Well, what did the old monk want?

He tops up both goblets, which they drink from on and off throughout the scene

NORFRYTH

Brought a message from the King, and he's coming back for an answer. The King wants us to improve his image. He doesn't like being called Edward the Confessor any more.

GURTH

What! It's a bit late for that. He's always been Edward the Confessor. What's brought all this on?

NORFRYTH

Well, he's picked up on the saying 'Confession is good for the soul, but bad for the reputation'. So from now on the word 'Confessor' is OUT. He wants to go down in history as Edward The Something Else.

GURTH

Oh, Lordy, Lordy. So after all this time he wants to be called Edward the Something Bloody Else. And he wants us to come up with the 'Something Else'?

NORFRYTH

Yep. Well, his dad Ethelred was saddled with 'The Unready' all his life. How would you like to go down in the chronicles as 'Gurth the Gormless'?

GURTH

Hell, no!. The King's an idiot, but you can't say, 'From now on, my lord you will be known as Edward, Prince of Pricks.

NORFRYTH

No way! I've become too attached to my tackle for that!

(He looks fondly downwards)

GURTH

The King changes his mind more often than he

changes his underwear – Have you stood near him lately, dear boy?

Gurth rolls his eyes and fans his face with his hand expressively.

NORFRYTH

Not likely! Here, this will take the taste away…(tops up the goblets) Well, anyway let's start with what we can't say.

GURTH

O.K. He was a right bastard to his poor mater.

NORFRYTH

BUT – she was a spiteful old cow herself.

GURTH

So 'a good boy to his mother' is out then. What else?

NORFRYTH

Well, he goes to France a lot.

GURTH

That's bad! Jolly unpatriotic, what? Next?

NORFRYTH

Well, he married young Edith, a right tastymorsel… phwaw!…I'll drink to the yummy Edith.
(they drink again)

216

GURTH

...but he never slept with her. Said he was too busy
with monks and stuff.

NORFRYTH

So it was more, 'Hello, Brother' than 'Hello, 'Sailor'?
Hmmmm...

GURTH

Well, he's never lifted my tabard. But he thinks the
royal dangler's just for sprinkling his thyme and
parsley from the battlements. Shame, really.

NORFRYTH

Then there's the pilgrimage to see the Pope. The King was
going, then changed his mind. Really got up the holy hooter.

GURTH

And now to make up for it the King says he'll rebuild
that old church on the Thames. He's on a hiding to
nothing down there. The land's a bog. Anything he
builds will just sink into the mud.

Gurth gestures with both hands to show something sinking,
and continues:
Glug...glug...and even more glug

NORFRYTH

He wants to call it Westminster Abbey, and, wait for it,

then wants to be buried there!

GURTH

...to be resurrected on the next high tide! Here's to the King's resur.... resur...resurrection...

NORFRYTH

...to the King's... erection...

Gurth gives Norfryth a funny look. They drink.

NORFRYTH

OK, so we never refer to this bloody old church of his.

GURTH

Nope. That just leaves us with finding him a new moniker.

NORFRYTH

Don't ask me. Edward 'The Holy'?, 'The Sublime'?, 'The Magnificent'?.

GURTH

Nah! What about 'King Edward the pain in the butt'?

They both giggle childishly

NORFRYTH

Don't be silly. The monk's coming back soon for an

answer. Think, man, think!

GURTH

No, give us a top-up first.

They fall silent thinking, and have another swig.

GURTH

O.K. Well, what about 'King Edward the Fantastic'?

Norfryth thinks a bit more and strokes his beard

NORFRYTH

Fan-trast-ic. Edward the Fan-trast-ic. Hm, O.K. I'll go with that. From this time forward King Edward will never, never, never be known as 'The Confessor', but as 'Edward the Fantrastic'.

GURTH

Don't shound quite right? And this so-called abbey of his will shink into the river and will never be mentioned or heard of, or heard of (repeating it much too loudly) AGAIN!

NORFRYTH

Shertainly not. Never. No, not never, never, never...

GURTH

I just said that.

Well, my son, I think we've cracked it. History will know our king as 'Edward the Flantrastic', and by no other name. Nooooo other, nooo other. Nooo...what was I saying?

NORFRYTH

And this Abbey place never was and never will be! Never was!

GURTH

Nope. Never! Not in a...mill...millililly... not for a long time.

A young servant appears at the door.

SERVANT

The holy man is here to see you, sirs.

GURTH

OK, wheel in the good monk, my poppet my liddle, liddle poppet. Inny got lovely eyes, Norwood? No, inny? Inny, though?

Gurth is absorbed in watching the young servant leave, then they both stand up unsteadily, drain their wine goblets, and give each other a high five at the second attempt.

FADE OUT

DARK SCREEN. FOUR LINES OF PRINT APPEAR IN
SUCCESSION

HISTORICAL NOTE
EDWARD WAS ALWAYS KNOWN AS THE CONFESSOR
WESTMINSTER ABBEY IS STILL STANDING
NORFRYTH WAS SEPARATED FROM HIS TACKLE AT
THE BATTLE OF HASTINGS

ANOTHER DARK SCREEN. THEN ONE LINE APPEARS

AND GURTH MOVED TO BRIGHTON

END

3 Not Carriage Trade

EXT. Street view of an old-fashioned shop front, signed
'Dumpling and Son of King's Lynn – Antiques and Curios.
Pawnbrokers'.

INT. *An untidy room behind the shop, one window, barred,*
large, old-fashioned safe is visible. The ancient Dumpling Sen.
behind a desk squinting at something under an Anglepoise
lamp through a jeweller's loupe. A buzzer sounds.
It's Dumpling Junior, Jack, in the shop.

DUMPLING
Yes, Jack. What is it?

JACK
Got a lady here, Dad. Got a few things to sell or pawn
or something. Wants you to have a look at them.

DUMPLING
Can you bring 'em in?

JACK
She wants to bring 'em herself. Says her knees are
playing up and she'd like to sit down.

DUMPLING
Well, can't she sit down out there? Grandad's chair's
still in the shop.

JACK

No, she wants to bring the stuff in herself.

DUMPLING

(lowers voice)

She's all right, is she?

JACK

(also lowered voice)

Oh, I think so. Just not exactly what you call 'carriage trade'. More like something swept up after the beet harvest.

DUMPLING

OK, Jack. Bring the lady in.

Dumpling presses a switch on his desk and Jack (who is the wrong side of 60) comes in with a short, overcoated elderly woman who walks badly and carries two Tesco polybags. Her speech is broad 'Norfolk'.

DUMPLING

Bring the lady a chair, Jack.

The bag lady sits down heavily opposite Dumpling.

DUMPLING

And you are, Madam?

223

PEGGY

Well, Sir, I'm Mrs Rummage, but just about everyone calls me Peggy.

DUMPLING

Fine, Mrs Rummage. Now what can we do for you?

PEGGY

Well, Sir, I've got a few bits and pieces here, thought I might pawn them for a bit.

Dumpling looks at Jack then wearily up to the ceiling.

DUMPLING

All right, Jack, I think you can leave us.

Jack returns to the shop.

DUMPLING

Now, Mrs Rummage...?

Peggy unwraps something in newspaper from her bag and lays it before Dumpling. It's a brooch of multicoloured stones with a small portrait in the centre. Dumpling holds the brooch in the palm of his hand and gives it a cursory look.

DUMPLING

Afraid we haven't got much here. It's a modern paste brooch, trying to look older than it is.

Dumpling picks up his loupe and examines the back of the brooch, then laughs.

DUMPLING

Just as I thought. They've even marked it in imitation of Fabergé.

PEGGY

Is that good?

DUMPLING

Well, it might have been if it hadn't been made in China and picked up at a car boot sale within the last couple of years.

PEGGY

Did you see the little picture?

DUMPLING

Yes, I saw it. Someone with a dark beard. Looks like Gerry Adams. It's just a photocopy.

PEGGY

So what do you think…?

DUMPLING

To pawn, the best is ten pounds.

PEGGY

All right, if that's the best I'll have to settle for that.

DUMPLING

Anything else?

Peggy unwraps another parcel and brings out a length of blue silk. There is an ornate badge sewn to the end of it.

PEGGY

What about this?

DUMPLING

No, sorry Mrs Rummage. I once took in an Orange Order sash, and once something from the Order of the Buffaloes, but I really don't deal in textiles. You'll have to take that one home with you, I'm afraid. Now I am rather busy, so if there's nothing else…

Peggy fumbles in the wrappings again and produces a rolled-up pair of white stockings.

DUMPLING

What's this? A pair of bedsocks? Oh, really, Mrs Rummage, I've told you we don't take textiles.

PEGGY

These have some embroidery at the tops, 'A.E.' and a little crown.

DUMPLING

Well, it's nicely embroidered, I grant you. Someone's initials I suppose or an old maker's trade mark. I still wouldn't want them.

Peggy wraps them up again and put them back into the bag.

PEGGY

Well, there's a few old records, suppose you'd call them vinyl.

Peggy pulls out some 78s and a few singles.

DUMPLING

Ah, now this looks more interesting. You were obviously a fan of Tom Jones, (looking through the records), oh, and some early Beatles! That's better! But you really shouldn't have scrawled your name all over the sleeves. That greatly reduces their value. Even so, I could let you have thirty pounds on these.

PEGGY

Yes, I'll take that.

DUMPLING

Nothing else? No early Norwich City programmes, anything like that? No early books by Delia Smith?

PEGGY

No, sorry.

DUMPLING

Good. That makes forty pounds in all then. My son will make out the ticket for you and give you the forty pounds from his float in the shop.

Dumpling presses the switch and speaks to Jack on the intercom.

DUMPLING

Forty pounds for Mrs Rumpstead and the usual ticket.

PEGGY

Rummage, Sir...

DUMPLING

Of course, Mrs ...er... Rummage. Thank yoooo...

Jack comes in and ushers out Peggy. Without another look Dumpling quickly goes back to examining something under the lamp.

FADE TO EXT. *Peggy leaves the shop and waddles down the road a short distance where a Range Rover is waiting by the kerb. There are two Labradors behind the dog guard. Peggy gets into the passenger seat, huffing and puffing. We don't see the driver at first until Peggy turns to her. Then we see that the driver is a well-preserved elderly lady in Barbour jacket and headscarf.*

LADY

How did it go?

PEGGY

Not bad. Forty pounds in all, ma'am.

LADY

Just drop it in the clean poo bag in the dash then, Peggy. (She does so.) Thanks. We'll redeem whatever you've left in a couple of months. So what did Mr Dumpling have to say?

PEGGY

He thought the Fabergé brooch was a fake, and that Tsar Nicholas was Gerry Adams.

LADY

Silly man. What about Queen Alexandra's Garter ribbon?

PEGGY

Not interested. Doesn't take textiles. Might have taken one from the Buffaloes, though.

LADY

Don't think I've heard of them. Must look them up the

the Almanach de Gotha. What about the bedsocks?

PEGGY

No sale. Even with King Edward's initials and the crown, the penny still didn't drop.

LADY

Ah well. And Princess Margaret's records?

PEGGY

Thirty pounds for those. Would have been more if her Royal Highness hadn't written her name on the sleeves in felt tip.

LADY

Pity. I was always telling Margaret not to do that. Still, it's not bad, Peggy.

PEGGY

No. Ma'am.

LADY

Well, let's head back home. I think we deserve a cup of tea.

PEGGY

Yes, ma'am. I'll put the kettle on as soon as we get home.

Lady starts the car and they drive off.

FADE

END

4 Sun-Dried

FADE IN

THE HOLY LAND,
VERY EARLY YEARS OF FIRST CENTURY

EXT. *A stony semi-desert scene, outside a primitive stone house Levi is sitting knapping a piece of stone, Nathan walks up carrying an 18-inch-square stone tablet, and scratching it with a stylus.*

LEVI

Whatcha doing?

NATHAN

Sudoku.

LEVI

Well, sudoku you, too.

NATHAN

I wasn't swearing, you fool, It's a game. The three kings brought it from the east. From Orientar to be precise.

LEVI

What? Hear no evil, see no evil, speak no evil?

NATHAN

No, that's the three wise monkeys. Honestly, you are a buffoon.

LEVI

So I am right. A buffoon is a sorta monkey.

NATHAN

That's a baboon, you ape. No, second thoughts, just leave it at twat, or we shall be here all night.

LEVI

Where'd you get to last night? You said you'd come with me to stone the unfaithful wife.

NATHAN

Was it good?

LEVI

You missed nothing! It was a shit evening.

NATHAN

So? She popped her clogs straight away?

LEVI

Worse than that. I'd only lobbed in a couple and then the silly cow repented so we all went home. What about you?

NATHAN

I went to this gig up in the hills.

LEVI

Who was playing?

NATHAN

They're called The Dead Sea Scrollers. They knock out tunes on these big jars.

LEVI

What about the talent?

NATHAN

I should say. This tasty dish Rebecca gave this ram's horn a good blow.

LEVI

I'd like to have seen that. Wish that I had my own wheels.

NATHAN

And then, and then she only gets out these jugs and smites them with the jaw-bone of an ass. Sweet, it was. Called 'An Arrangement for Five Jars and a Couple of Jugs'. Lovely!

LEVI

I wish I understood good music! Big crowd?

NATHAN

Nah. A lot had gone down to the Jordan to see that baptising johnny. The geezer who lives on locusts and wild honey.

LEVI

What's his name?

NATHAN

I just told you, thicko – Baptising Johnny. He's started a craze for locusts. Now they bring 'em in from Egypt by the camel load.

LEVI

Ugh! I wouldn't let a foreign locust pass my lips.

NATHAN

Oh, these are sun-dried, top of the range. Well, you'd need an educated palate, so that lets you out!

LEVI

You've no room to talk! The only time you eat decent food is when the rabbi slips your missus a bit of sacrificial goat out of his back passage.

NATHAN

Jealousy will get you nowhere. Hello, what's all this?

An elderly man, Ephraim, pulls up pulling a light one-man chariot, taking the place of a donkey between its shafts.

NATHAN

Hi, Ephraim! Where's your moke then?

LEVI

If he's anything like his owner, he's well knackered.

EPHRAIM

You boys can laugh. He passed over to the other side.

LEVI

You mean he's snuffed it?

EPHRAIM

No, a scorpion stung him on the butt and he didn't stop running till he got to Egypt.

NATHAN

Tough.

EPHRAIM

Oh, it could be worse. He got mixed up with a camel race and came in first, so I won a prize.

NATHAN

Which was?

EPHRAIM

Big pack of sun-dried locusts. Top of the range.

NATHAN

You jammy old codger! What with the wheels now, then?

EPHRAIM

I'll flog 'em.

NATHAN

There y'are, Levi. Just borrow your dad's donkey, and you're rolling!

Levi and Nathan walk round the chariot kicking the wheels and looking unenthusiastic.

EPHRAIM

Only nineteen careful owners, last one was the high priest's mother who just used it for shopping.

LEVI

Who you kidding? This is old gladiator stock out of the Coliseum over in Rome.

NATHAN

He's right. Look here – sword marks. And here, look, lions' teeth marks on the vinyl.

EPHRAIM

Exactly. The lion's the king of beasts. That puts you a cut above the guys with vinyl just gnawed by the starving beggars.

LEVI

I never thought of that. And what's this here, in the foot-well?

EPHRAIM

Oh, they're blood stains.

LEVI

That's cool! And these brown ones down here?

EPHRAIM

Ah, the gladiators make those marks when they see the lions let loose.

LEVI

I'm liking this more and more.

NATHAN

And what's that smell?

EPHRAIM

Oh, I had a touch of cystitis.

LEVI

Great! It all reminds me of my granddad's place. How much is it?

EPHRAIM

Well, give us your tickets to the next wife stoning, and it's yours.

LEVI

Done! Now I can go to the gigs in the hills, learn about good music and get cultured.

EPHRAIM

Well, I must be off. Missus is stewing a bit of goat for tonight, got it off the rabbi, the randy old sod. Don't like to think what the wife had to do to get it though. See you tomorrow for those tickets.

Ephraim goes off

LEVI

Well, well, well. Now we know how some people get to have goat for supper. What did your missus do to earn hers, Nathan? What's she been giving the randy rabbi in return, Nathan?

NATHAN

Oh, piss off!
Levi continues inspecting the chariot and brings out a box.

LEVI

See what I've found in the glove box – a pack of sun-dried locusts. Want one, Nathan? They're top of the range. Came from 'the Pharaoh's grocer' in town.

NATHAN

No I don't! I'm going home for my donkey castrator and then to call on the rabbi.

LEVI

See you tomorrow then?

NATHAN

Sure. Bring your sun-dried locusts. By then I might be able to contribute some sort of offal to the feast.

LEVI

Well, locust and offals! I'll try anything once.

NATHAN

And I'll make sure everything is sun-dried.

Nathan goes, leaving Levi patting his new chariot and sampling the locusts to his evident enjoyment.

LEVI

Upwardly mobile at last! Can't wait for tomorrow.

END

Some Local History

A medicine maker comes to Horsham

It was in April 1934 that a local estate agent King and Chasemore put up a parcel of land for sale at Horsham Town Hall, advertised as 'ripe for factory or building development'. There were 19 acres that ran alongside Parsonage Road, currently let out to Mr W.J. Standing as a market garden. The Swiss chemical firm of CIBA had bought a Manchester dyestuffs company in 1911 and had set up a small subsidiary pharmaceutical department in south-east London shortly afterwards. (In those pioneering days dyestuffs businesses were the midwife to the pharmaceutical industry since they usually started from the same basic chemical ingredients.)

The young business flourished, and by 1934 the management had ideas of moving out of London and building a brand new factory to make their medicines and to do everything else on one site. It turned out to be a wise move, as six years later the London premises were fire-bombed to the ground. As a desirable location Horsham had plenty of competition, and the managers considered umpteen other sites including Sidcup, Maidstone, St. Mary Cray and Welwyn. The factory would need a good water supply, road and rail links. The company took out an option to purchase the Horsham land but it wasn't until 1937 that a 250-foot borehole proved beyond doubt that water supply would be no problem.

In April 1938 the first contracts for the driveway and the two entrance lodges were signed with London architects O'-Donoghue and Halfhide of Upper Grosvenor Street. The high specification of the driveway alone astonished everyone, one man asserting that it was as good or better than the main road to London. This gave a clue that CIBA had already set a gold-standard of quality for whatever they were to build at Horsham. Logically enough, the roadside lodges were designated Buildings 1 and 2. But it was the all-purpose edifice itself with its central tower, echoing Giles Gilbert Scott's Cambridge Library of 1934 and ever to be known as Building 3, of course, that took the breath away and over the years has become recognized as an art deco jewel to rival anything in that style anywhere else in the country.

The staircase within the impressive central tower is illuminated from outside by glass bricks, while inside it the great bronze and glass chandelier is another classic piece of art deco design. The whole of the interior is clad in beautiful Travertine stone from quarries near Rome, and the supporting pillars faced in contrasting richly veined dark and polished marbles. The tower also served a practical purpose, since it originally concealed a chimney which took smoke from the boilers in the basement. Coal or coke delivered to the company's railway siding was fed by an underground conveyor straight into the boiler room beneath the entrance hall, where a visitor might just detect a slight rumbling when the conveyor was working. During wartime the tower made a great look-out, and in daylight the commissionaire would go to the top to spot enemy aircraft, to warn the staff and to put out a flag so that a watcher at Collyer's School a couple of fields away could also pick up his danger signal.

The building, not quite finished as war broke out in 1939, was still echoing to the operatic arias of Italian craftsmen laying the floors, while back in London the heat was on, and CIBA managed to hire a greengrocer's van to cart their finished medicines down to Horsham at £2.50 a trip. Only the two lodges were complete, so a handful of Londoners struggled to squeeze the packing cases into their tiny space.

Soon the great building itself was ready and it was here that manufacturing in Horsham began. On the ground floor they started producing pharmaceutical chemicals, a process that in 1951 was transferred to a new factory that the Horsham staff set up near Grimsby. The first floor of Building 3 was devoted to making and packaging a variety of medicines, while everything else, including an elegant boardroom-cum-library, occupied the top floor. During the war a secret Army convoy sometimes drove up in the dead of night to collect medical supplies for use by the Allies on the world's battlefields.

Over the years the manufacturing and storage facilities at Horsham were expanded many times over by CIBA and then by Ciba-Geigy. The first biochemical research unit was opened on the site in May1965 and others followed, lastly under the management of Novartis, the name the company adopted after Ciba-Geigy had been joined by a third great Swiss pharma company, Sandoz. So as the world changes so the pages keep turning, often illuminated by the light of great achievement, sometimes stained with tears, and always with the hope of better things ahead. Mr Standing's market garden had come an awfully long way since it was just growing cabbages.

Novartis withdrew from Horsham in 2014 eventually leaving only the art deco building standing.

A Millennium Perspective
'The Dome'

Readers who are 'over the hill' and retired, like me, may sometimes see a quiz called *Fifteen to One* which once appeared at four o'clock daily on Channel 4. I find that I am often rocked to the socks by the contestants' ignorance of the history of our own country. Those on *University Challenge* often do little better. Lest this should sound supercilious, I must add that I would be equally dumb if asked about football, popular music, films, and a good deal of science. Over the years I have gone from being a young fogey to an old fogey in one easy, downhill movement.

Fortunately, if the deficiencies in today's school syllabus are to blame, they are often made up in part by the simple process of getting older. Those of us who lived through the last war are likely to know a bit about that particular topic because of our own experience, but go back another fifty years, say, and we are in the same position as any twenty-year-old – relying on what we have been taught, read, or just picked up somehow.

I think it's in *Summoned By Bells* that John Betjeman recalls school assembly in the First War, when the headmaster regularly gives out the names of former schoolboys who have been killed in the war, his voice wavering with emotion. It was the same in my own day at Collyer's, when that redoubtable headmaster P.A. Tharp would read at assembly the news of boys reported as casualties in the Second War, some only out of school a matter of months.

Tharp's face took on a look of sad resignation, mouth tightly drawn at the corners, no doubt resolute, as a great advocate of the 'stiff upper lip', not to let his voice betray him as Betjeman's master's had. It's not so much that history repeats itself, it's simply that the common thread is always our humanity, or the human situation.

This is why history, if it does nothing else, compels us to empathize with our forebears and marvel at what they achieved in the face of appalling difficulties. For millions who have gone before us Hobbes's dictum about sums it up, life was 'poor, nasty, brutish and short'. Only comparatively recently have the majority in these islands ceased to find it a pretty rocky road on that journey from birth to the grave. My mother knew a lady who years ago had been a cook at a 'big house' in Wisborough Green. The lady lived in Horsham, so she walked to Wisborough Green and back every day. One admits that this verges on the unbelievable, since both ways it's nearly 20 miles, but maybe the 'big house' was not quite all the way to Wisborough Green.

People in earlier years were certainly made of sterner stuff than we are, and, what's more, they were mostly happy, decent, honest, and, in a word, good. Mention to those people vandalism, road rage or child abuse and they would first ask you to translate, and when you had done so they would wonder what pit of Hell you had emerged from and suggest you board the next carter's wagon and go back there.

OK – I've exaggerated. Just being unsophisticated and dead doesn't make people saints, but who can deny that contentment and personal peace are two gifts that our fore-bears possessed that we have managed to mislay? If you doubt that, look around you. Whatever appears in the Millennium Dome, the organizers will have little to say about either of those two attributes. And if history gets a look-in, it will probably be for the wrong reasons. When the time comes, instead of chasing off to see the Dome, why not have another walk around our St. Mary's Church, and marvel at how the tiny community of Horsham over the centuries managed to build on such a scale. And spare a thought for those whose remains lie in the churchyard. Some of those could be history's real heroes and their example could have much to teach Millennium Man. But when it comes to moralizing in churchyards I guess that one Thomas Gray has beaten me to it.

The Prisoner of War Camp at Coolhurst

I don't know how people living in Horsham came to know about the camp – most likely by word of mouth. It was probably in 1944 that my mother, my aunt and cousin and I went up to the forest to see the camp. I guess that I was about 13 at the time and attending Collyer's School. My cousin would have been about five. All one saw of the camp was a wired enclosure immediately behind St. John the Evangelist Church. Access was across some open ground to the east end of the church.

The attraction was that the prisoners were 'selling' toys that they had made from the abundant supply of wood. The toys were fairly crude 'folk' creations. I came away with a plaything consisting of three pecking chicken on a board shaped like a table tennis bat, their heads activated by three weights suspended through a hole in the board. The currency was packets of cigarettes.

As I remember, the prisoners were dressed in brown. We thought that they were Italian. The wire must have had a fairly wide mesh to allow the transactions to take place. I don't remember seeing any huts or observation towers to confirm the popular image of a prison camp. I also don't recall seeing any troops or guards, although there must have been a few of them around.

'Like a Couple of Intertwining Vines'

Horsham's oldest surviving institution is surely the Church, and St. Mary's is the (we hope) enduring symbol of it. But where must we look to find the runner-up in the Horsham History Stakes? Surely, the prize money for second place must go to Collyer's, formerly 'The Grammar School', now the College of Richard Collyer in Horsham. The foundation date of Collyer's is reckoned to be 1532, the year that Richard Collyer (or Collier) signed the will that endowed his school. So one need not have attended Collyer's to work out that Collyer's the institution is about half the age of the Parish Church. Over the centuries both institutions have grown in Horsham like a couple of intertwining vines, and both have developed and changed over the centuries to such an extent that Richard Collyer and Roger of Wallingford (the first identified Vicar) would be astonished to see their respective institutions today. Collyer never saw his at all, of course – such is the fate of all testatory benefactors!

It is tempting to muse that Richard Collyer's story is one of 'rags to riches', and it probably is. He was born in or around Horsham, and is first heard of on his way up as a merchant in the Mercers' Company, the great City guild that today is the premier City livery company and one of great beneficence and substance. By the time Collyer made his will he also had amassed wealth and property, and, motivated by the spirit of the age, 'Christian charity' featured prominently in his will.

One of his many bequests was to build a school-house for

sixty Horsham boys, and although the Mercers were to be the trustees of the funds, the Vicar and Churchwardens of Horsham were to be responsible for the school's management, which included the selection of the scholars and the appointment of the headmaster and usher. Thus it was that the Church in Horsham became deeply involved in the birth of Collyer's, and played a major part in its development through the following centuries. To this day, the Vicar (or Team Rector, as he is now) is an *ex officio* governor.

Although by 1532 Henry's row with the Pope was near to boiling over, the Catholic piety underlying Collyer's will is unmistakable. He not only left money for the Horsham clergy to pray for his soul, but also, as a *quid pro quo* for being educated, desired that the children at the school should do the same. The vicissitudes of the school and its relations with the Church, the people of Horsham, and the Mercers' Company are chronicled by the late Austin Willson in his scholarly and entertaining work, *A History of Collyer's School 1532 to 1964*, a treasure trove that has been shamelessly plundered to produce this article. (Somehow, I don't think he would mind, as he was my own history master during my time at Collyer's, and is universally remembered with great affection.)

When the Grammar School was eventually built, as befits a school with close links with the Church, it lay almost within the shadow of St. Mary's, roughly on the site of today's St. Mary's School. In spite of alteration and rebuilding, the School finally outgrew its premises in Denne Road, and new buildings were opened on its present Hurst

Road site in the April of 1893.

The School adopted the insignia of the Mercers' Company, 'The Maiden', with the motto *Honor Deo*. This most ancient of symbols, probably dating back to early in the Fourteenth Century, was once thought to depict The Virgin, and it would have made a neat conclusion to highlight the connexion between St. Mary's Church, the Company and its Virgin, and Collyer's. But alas and alack! The Maiden probably started out as a trade sign to symbolize the Mercers' wares, honouring the ladies who made them, and the wealthier ones who would be wearing them. In spite of the now supposed secular origin of the Collyer's erstwhile 'Virgin', the school has nevertheless done its bit to swell 'the household of faith', including producing one saint, at least two bishops, and enough clergy to pack a handful of vestries. But that, as they say… is another story.

Index
John's Jottings, Apologia, Apologia Plus and Some Local History